D0623898

THE METROPOLITAN WATER DISTRICT OF SOUTHERN CALIFORNIA

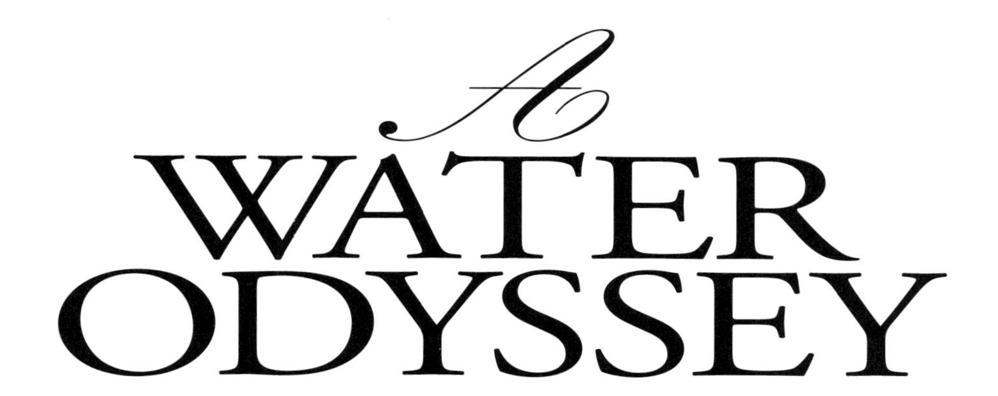

A Water Odyssey

The Story
of
Metropolitan Water District
of Southern California

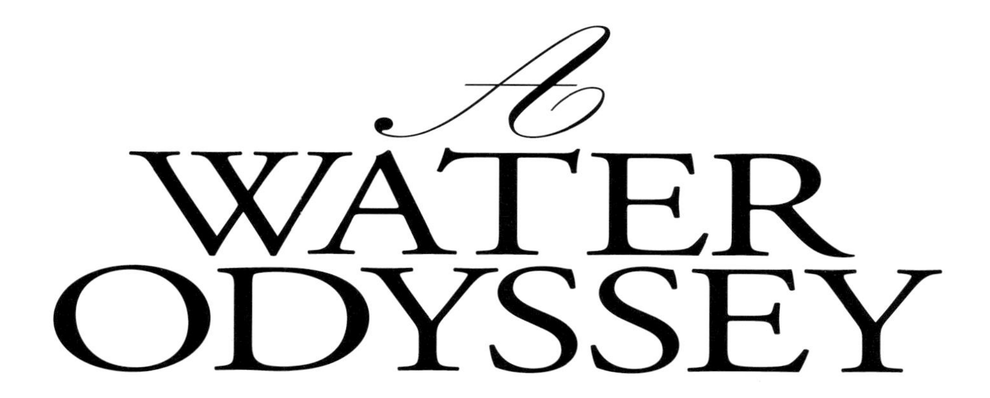

The Story
of
Metropolitan Water District
of Southern California

1991

By Joel Schwarz

Commemorating 50 Years of Water Delivery
to Southern California

C R E D I T S

Editor and Addenda Writer: JoAnn Lundgren

Design: Mario Chavez

Photography Coordination: Patrick Knisely

Additional Editing: Roselle Lewis

Contributing Photographers: Jeffrey Belt, Mario Chavez, Jeff Corwin, Robert Dawson, Lois Gervais, Tony Hertz, Patrick Knisely, David LoCicero, Laurie Metzger, Rick Ravenstine, Ernesto Rodriguez.

Photos provided by: Bancroft Library, U.C. Berkeley; Bureau of Reclamation; California Historical Society Collection, University of Southern California; California State Archives; California State Library; City of Los Angeles Department of Water and Power; Creative Visuals; East Bay Municipal Utility District; Imperial Irrigation District; J.W. Powell Memorial Museum, Page, Arizona; Los Angeles Chamber of Commerce; Los Angeles Times History Center; McDonnell Douglas/ Douglas Aircraft Company; New York Yankees; Security Pacific Collection/Los Angeles Public Library; Southwest Museum; State of California Department of Parks and Recreation; California Department of Water Resources; Title Insurance Collection; Tournament of Roses.

Illustrations and Maps: Will Burlingame and Raphael Montoliu.

Digital Film Output: PrePress Studio

Printing: Monarch Litho

Book Binder: Hiller Books & Binders

Printed in the United States of America on recycled and recyclable paper.

BOARD OF DIRECTORS BY MEMBER AGENCY

Chairman
LOIS B. KRIEGER

Vice Chairman
MARILYN GARCIA

Vice Chairman
HARRY GRIFFEN

Vice Chairman
KENNETH H. WITT

Secretary
JOHN KILLEFER

Anaheim
BOB KAZARIAN

Beverly Hills
INA S. ROTH

Burbank
LARRY L. STAMPER

Compton
REGINA TURNEY-MURPH

Fullerton
JAMES H. BLAKE

Glendale
JAMES M. REZ

Long Beach
IDA FRANCES LOWRY

Los Angeles
ROBERT J. ABERNETHY
ALF W. BRANDT
MICHAEL J. GAGE
MARILYN GARCIA
EDWARD L. KUSSMAN
S. DELL SCOTT
HELEN ROMERO SHAW
VERNON R. WATKINS

Pasadena
TIMOTHY F. BRICK

San Fernando
DOUDE WYSBEEK

San Marino
JOHN T. MORRIS

Santa Ana
DANIEL H. YOUNG

Santa Monica
CHRISTINE E. REED

Torrance
MARVIN BREWER

Calleguas Municipal Water District
PATRICK H. MILLER
CARL E. WARD

Central Basin Municipal Water District
DOUGLAS W. FERGUSON
E. THORNTON IBBETSON
LEONIS C. MALBURG

Chino Basin Municipal Water District
ANNE W. DUNIHUE
BILL M. HILL

Coastal Municipal Water District
JOHN KILLEFER
WAYNE T. McMURRAY

Eastern Municipal Water District
DOYLE F. BOEN

Foothill Municipal Water District
BROOKS T. MORRIS

Las Virgenes Municipal Water District
A. MACNEIL STELLE

Municipal Water District of Orange County
WILLIAM F. DAVENPORT
JOHN V. FOLEY
M. ROY KNAUFT JR.
CARL J. KYMLA
KENNETH H. WITT

San Diego County Water Authority
HARRY GRIFFEN
FRANCESCA M. KRAUEL
MICHAEL D. MADIGAN
DALE MASON
JOHN P. STARKEY
HERBERT H. STICKNEY

Three Valleys Municipal Water District
BRUCE R. J. MILNE

Upper San Gabriel Valley Municipal Water District
BURTON E. JONES
JOHN E. MAULDING

West Basin Municipal Water District
CHARLES D. BARKER
ROBERT GOLDSWORTHY
CHARLES L. STUART

Western Municipal Water District of Riverside County
LOIS B. KRIEGER

Lois B. Krieger

Marilyn Garcia

Harry Griffen

Kenneth H. Witt

John Killefer

Chairman of the Board Lois B. Krieger and General Manager Carl Boronkay

It is altogether fitting to mark, by a recounting of its history, this special anniversary of the Metropolitan Water District — 50 years of delivery of water to Southern California. That history is both colorful and dramatic, for water development like any far-reaching social policy, draws many to the issue and excites emotions. In California, one can trace the history of most major areas and, indeed, the state as a whole, with the parallel history of water supply.

In the case of Southern California, the banding together of thirteen cities, later to be joined by other cities and public agencies responsible for water supply, represents today a model that is being examined elsewhere in this state and in other states.

The success of Metropolitan is owed to the many thousands of men and women who played a role in its creation and achievements. To them this history is dedicated.

PREFACE

The economy, indeed existence, of the near-desert region that is Southern California is dependent upon imported water. The early 20th century saw construction by the City of Los Angeles of an aqueduct to carry water from the Owens Valley. Then in the late 1920s, a still rapidly growing Los Angeles joined together with 10 surrounding smaller cities to form the Metropolitan Water District of Southern California. The new district, which would number 13 cities by the time construction started, would build the Colorado River Aqueduct and distribute the water it carried to augment local rivers and groundwater and Los Angeles' imported supplies.

Having grown to become one of the world's largest water suppliers, Metropolitan consists of 27 member agencies: 14 cities, 12 municipal water districts and one county water authority. The municipal water districts and the authority, in turn, supply water to subagencies for retailing. Included within district boundaries, some 5,200 square miles in six counties, are more than 130 incorporated cities as well as many large unincorporated areas.

Metropolitan's primary sources of supply are imports from Northern California through the State Water Project and from the Colorado River through its own aqueduct. It provides more than half of the water used by some 15 million Southern Californians.

In reading this history marking 50 years of water deliveries to the Southland by the Metropolitan Water District, one will pause at intervals in awe of the difficulties encountered over time and the resourcefulness of those who overcame them. Certainly the challenge of augmenting the natural attractions of the region with a secure water supply was an exciting one and explains the distinguished individuals who assumed leadership positions. That excitement also was felt by the thousands of employees who took pride in contributing to Metropolitan's accomplishments — a pride that continues today.

The early challenges were physical and financial and drew upon the expertise and experience of all those involved without the benefit of modern engineering tools, computers or construction machinery. Metropolitan's success is evidenced not simply by its own impressive importation and distribution facilities (the Colorado River Aqueduct has been the subject of numerous accolades and awards) and those of the State Water Project in which we are an active partner. Rather, its success is defined, more comprehensively, by the growth and prosperity of our region and, as a consequence, the state itself. Southern California's economy is the envy of the nation with an annual gross regional product of about $400 billion and nearly 7.5 million jobs. Were we a nation, we would rank tenth in wealth among the industrial nations of the world.

But today, praise is mixed with criticism as some seek to judge past achievements by changed or changing values. So we hear from those who, taking water availability and our related high standard of living for granted, focus on harm done to the natural environment and assail those they believe responsible — often water officials.

The policy of early century California, as elsewhere, was development or utilization of our natural resources for agricultural and municipal pursuits. But, of course, that policy is subject to review and change and we are indeed in such a period; witness the change in attitude regarding maintaining an historic level of Mono Lake with freshwater flows that have been diverted for years to help supply drinking water to the residents of the city of Los Angeles. Thus, we have become more sensitive to the degradation of air and water quality, damage to fish and wildlife and, indeed, the various lifestyle encroachments generated by an ever-increasing population. These concerns should cause us to examine carefully their root causes and search for remedies. But, it is both fruitless and unfair to simply criticize those who, through extraordinary efforts, carried out public policy as it existed.

Society may have been insufficiently sensitive, in creating its infrastructure, to what have emerged as well-accepted environmental values. And while we recognize this and should act to protect and even restore the environment, it must be done in the context of continuing responsibility to meet the water requirements of a rapidly growing California.

It is unfortunate that some refuse to accept this dual, intertwined objective and focus solely on environmental concerns. This narrow approach would seem to mirror the single-mindedness ascribed to those given the responsibility for meeting water needs.

The task today is for all of us to broaden our perspectives and goals, to no longer regard one dimension of a problem as the whole problem. Thus, environmentalists can no longer focus solely on the environment to the exclusion of legitimate water needs of the urban and agricultural communities; agricultural interests cannot concentrate simply on adequate water supplies for farm production; urban water suppliers cannot look only to the needs of their dependent municipalities.

Dividing society's water problems artificially among competing interests has been harmful to us all; it prevents finding true solutions to those problems. Perhaps descriptive of the current stalemate in resolution of our water problems is the statement of Governor Richard Lamm of Colorado referring to Colorado's warring water interests, "Water development has been an eye-for-an-eye, tooth-for-a-tooth situation that left us all toothless and blind."

Fortunately, responsible representatives of all three, so-called, interest communities have recognized that the old way of only fighting one another just doesn't work and are engaged in serious dialogue seeking comprehensive solutions. As we approach a new century, there are strong indications that an all-encompassing coalition can be created to fairly resolve our very serious environmental/water use problems.

With challenges that are different, but no less daunting, than those facing Metropolitan in its early years, let us hope that a commemoration 50 years from now will be warranted, that we and our successors will have met the high standards of vision and perseverance set by our predecessors.

Carl Boronkay

CARL BORONKAY
GENERAL MANAGER

TABLE OF CONTENTS

VII	*Dedication*
VIII	*Preface*
2	*Introduction*
6	*Chapter 1 - The Missing Ingredient*
14	*Chapter 2 - The Mulholland Legacy*
25	*Chapter 3 - The River*
37	*Chapter 4 - The Politics of Water*
44	*Chapter 5 - Picking the Route*
56	*Chapter 6 - Across the Sands and Through the Mountains*
78	*Chapter 7 - War and Peace, Annexation and Expansion*
90	*Chapter 8 - Other Needs, Other Systems*
102	*Chapter 9 - The Battle for Approval*
119	*Chapter 10 - Building a Water Lifeline*
136	*Chapter 11 - The Delta Quandary*
147	*Chapter 12 - The Canal That Wasn't*
160	*Chapter 13 - Stretching the Supply*
173	*Chapter 14 - A Taste of Quality*
180	*Chapter 15 - New Challenges and a New Century*
	Addenda:
189	*Leading the Way: Chairmen of the Board*
195	*Carrying Out the Mission: Profiles in Management*
202	*Reflections of Longtime Board Members*
210	*Index*

INTRODUCTION

A new era was about to dawn, but Southern Californians were too preoccupied to notice it.

June 17, 1941, was a typical late spring day. The air was clear and the word "smog" was yet to be coined. The temperature would peak at 78 degrees in downtown Los Angeles, 82 in nearby Pasadena where ceremonies were planned at Sunset Reservoir. Those ceremonies were modest, a seemingly incidental climax to a vast undertaking that had been launched 18 years earlier. One of North America's wildest rivers, the Colorado, had been tamed and an aqueduct and distribution system had been constructed to bring some of its waters more than 300 miles to Southern California.

The changing face of Los Angeles

Now as the first water from the river completed its journey through the Colorado River Aqueduct and the upper feeder, which connected Lake Mathews in Riverside County to Sunset Reservoir, only a handful of officials were present to commemorate the occasion. The district had received more attention the previous January when its float was awarded first place in the class of public utilities in the Rose Parade. The water delivery ceremonies originally had been scheduled for June 18. But when work was completed on the distribution system ahead of schedule, the ceremonies were advanced one day. The participants came from Pasadena and the Metropolitan Water District, accompanied by newspaper reporters and photographers. Water gushed into the reservoir through a series of inlet pipes and Robert Diemer, Metropolitan's distribution engineer, poured glasses of the liquid to toast the event. The rest of Pasadena's residents would have to wait several days before they got their first sip of Colorado River water. It took that long for the inflowing river water to mix with the existing supply in Sunset Reservoir and make its way through the water lines of Pasadena to individual homes.

Reports of the modest ceremonies were not exactly front page news on June 18. The Pasadena Star News played the story and two photographs

MWD coming up roses

at the top of page one of the paper's second section. There was no news coverage of the event to be found anywhere in the 36 pages of the Los Angeles Times. The Times did run an editorial, lauding the impending delivery of water later in the day. No one, apparently, had notified the Times that the ceremonies had been moved ahead.

In fairness, the attention of the press and most Southern Californians was fixed elsewhere. In the middle of 1941, the United States was still emerging from the Great Depression. The specter of another world war was looming ever larger on the horizon; fighting already had broken out in Europe and Asia. Newspapers were filled with stories and rumors of the growing conflict.

The spreading war wasn't the only thing on people's minds. Sports pages were filled with stories of the upcoming June 19th heavyweight championship fight between Joe Louis and challenger Billy Conn. Baseball's New

Orson Welles as Citizen Kane

York Yankees and Brooklyn Dodgers were headed toward pennants and the first ever subway World Series. And the Yankees' Joe DiMaggio was midway through his epic 56-game hitting streak.

On June 17, after a day of quiet trading, the Dow Jones Industrial average closed at 124. For 15 cents, movie patrons could catch a showing of "Citizen Kane" in its final two-week Los Angeles run or take in the "Road to Zanzibar" with Bing Crosby, Bob Hope and Dorothy Lamour. In the grocery store, fresh apricots were a nickel a pound, a two-pound can of coffee was 50 cents and center-cut sirloin steak was an advertised special at 29 cents a pound. The Southern California real estate boom was still far in the future — a three-bedroom, two-story English-style house in Pasadena was priced at $7,500.

But change, inexorable and dramatic, was coming to Southern California and all of California. In the decades ahead, one of the greatest internal migrations in history would occur as the region's population exploded. California was poised to become the most populous state in the union with an economy that would be larger than most nations'. To sustain this robust economy and millions of new citizens, an infrastructure of vital services was required, not least of which was a dependable supply of water. The job of acquiring that water was entrusted to the Metropolitan Water District in 1928 by the people in the cities it would serve.

June 17, 1941, was just one day in the long story of securing that supply. It is a narrative that begins before recorded history and one whose final chapters have yet to be written.

Joltin' Joe DiMaggio

CALIFORNIA WAS POISED TO BECOME THE MOST POPULOUS STATE IN THE UNION WITH AN ECONOMY THAT WOULD BE LARGER THAN MOST NATIONS'.

The landscape was a semidesert, sparsely vegetated with chaparral and oak, a land where spring's short-lived greenery quickly turned dusty-gray and leathery-brown because of lack of water.

Early Southern California resident

Chapter 1

THE MISSING INGREDIENT

It would have been difficult to mistake the land stretched out before them for the Garden of Eden. That day in 1542, Juan Rodriguez Cabrillo and his crew were the first Europeans to land on this soil they would claim for Spain and later call Alta California. The landscape was a semidesert, sparsely vegetated with chaparral and oak, a land where spring's short-lived greenery quickly turned dusty-gray and leathery-brown because of lack of water.

Juan Rodriguez Cabrillo

Yet, it was a land rich in natural resources save that vital one. The soil anchoring the roots of the valley and live oaks was fertile, game was plentiful and the waters and beaches of the Pacific Ocean offered generous bounty. Freshwater, however, was scarce and intermittent. And without a dependable supply, agriculture for the area's inhabitants was impossible to practice. Thus, they evolved subsistence cultures, often of the most meager kind.

The first people Cabrillo encountered were the Chumash, the largest of four major Indian groups inhabiting coastal Southern California. They lived in the area from San Luis Obispo south to Malibu Canyon and inland to the western margin of the San Joaquin Valley. Records of the Chumash culture are sparse, and estimates of the population inhabiting the land prior to the founding of the Spanish missions in the late 1700s range from 8,000 to 22,000. Food was particularly abundant for the Chumash along the Santa Barbara Channel, providing them with more leisure time than most California tribes. This allowed them to enjoy such activities as games, gambling, dancing and singing. In 1769, bands of Chumash entertained members of the Portola Expedition, which had been dispatched to explore the California coastline. One of them, Father Juan Crespi, recorded in his notebooks that the Chumash's "singing and music was pleasant but interminable."

South of the Chumash, lived the Gabrielino who occupied a good part of what today is Los Angeles and Orange counties, including the watershed of the Los Angeles, San Gabriel and Santa Ana rivers. Like the Chumash,

Farmers working the soil at the San Diego Mission

they hunted with bows and arrows, traps, snares and harpoons. The Luiseno Indians ranged from the area of Aliso Creek in Orange County down the coast into San Diego County and inland to Lake Elsinore and Temecula. The Luiseno and their neighbors to the south, the Dieguneo, were more warlike than the Chumash and the Gabrielino. The Dieguneo, whose territory extended as far south as Ensenada in what is today Mexico, were by far the fiercest. No tribe in California resisted the Spaniards' efforts to control and convert them more stubbornly. In 1775, some 800 Diegueno from 70 villages revolted, burned the San Diego Mission and killed one priest.

In the years before the colonizing Spaniards arrived, life was simple and easy for Southern California's Native Americans. While the availability of water was capricious, there was an abundance of foodstuffs to gather, trap and hunt. The foundation of the Chumash, Gabrielino, Luiseno and Diegueno diet was the acorn. In the fall, the people collected ripened acorns from California's prolific oaks and stored them for year-round use. Acorns required water to make them palatable because of the bitter tannin they contained. The small nuts were pounded into meal with stone pestles and soaked in water to leach out the tannin. Then the meal was cooked as the nourishing staple of the natives' diet.

This subsistence culture made the early Southern Californians seminomadic. While they had permanent village sites located near usually reliable sources of water, the concept of growing food was unknown. Only the Luiseno, who are thought to have raised a little tobacco and wild onions as a result of coming into contact with natives along the Colorado River, had the barest hint of an agricultural tradition. As a result, the Native Americans were forced to scour the countryside each year for food and water.

Indian water bearers

It was a way of life that existed for centuries, but one fated to change quickly with the arrival of Europeans. Spain had shown little interest in California for more than 200 years following Cabrillo's voyage in 1542. It was a forgotten frontier. But stories of Russian and English incursions on the west coast of North America alarmed the Spanish. The Russians were drifting south from Alaska while the English, with their powerful navy and growing band of colonies on the Atlantic coast, had begun looking westward. In 1769, the new governor of Baja California, Gaspar de Portola, personally launched an expedition up the California coast to secure and settle it.

Accompanying Portola were soldiers, craftsmen, settlers and a group of Franciscan fathers headed by Junipero Serra, the expedition's spiritual leader. It was Serra, more than members of his group, who would shape California's early destiny and direction. In July 1769, the Portola expedition reached San Diego. Serra was left to build the first of a ribbon of 21 missions extending all the way to Sonoma that the Franciscans would construct. The main body of the expedition, meanwhile, continued northward to find Monterey Bay. On August 2, the Spanish arrived on the banks of a stream that was given the unwieldy name of Nuestra Senora la Reina de los Angeles de Porciuncula. After a pause, the expedition continued on. A dozen years would pass before the Spanish thought enough of the spot to occupy it. In 1781, 11 families were sent from Mexico to found a pueblo that later was to become known as Los Angeles.

Meanwhile the Franciscans were beginning their transformation of California. Unlike the natives, the Spanish were farmers, descendants of a culture long accustomed to irrigating fertile but dry land. Steeped in Mediterranean tradition, familiar with the way the Greeks and Romans built water works as a keystone of civilization, the Franciscans carried that work ethic to California.

Central to the padres tireless efforts to save souls and convert the Native Americans to Christianity was the establishment of missions. In mission churches and schools built by Franciscans, conversion and education were all important. Missionary efforts extended to the workers in the fields, orchards and vineyards planted by the padres. Laudable as the Franciscans' work may have been, the Spanish government was pragmatic and tight with a doubloon. Each of the missions was expected to be self-sufficient in five years. If not, the mission was either moved or abandoned.

Three women of the mission at San Luis Rey — all purportedly over 100 years old

So mission agriculture played a dual role — helping to provide economic stability, thereby enabling the Franciscans to "civilize" California's natives by putting them to work learning to grow crops from the land. Almost immediately the Franciscans came face to face with a California reality: while the soil may be rich, local water resources often are limited or inadequate. Making the land fruitful required facilities to gather, conserve and transport water to the mission fields. Within four years of the founding of Mission San Diego de Alcala, the padres and Indian workers under their direction dammed a creek and diverted its water through earthen ditches for six miles to irrigate the mission's fields.

In subsequent years, more water systems were built for San Fernando, San Luis Rey, La Purisma, Santa Barbara, San Gabriel and other missions. The padres succeeded in introducing agriculture to Southern California's natives, but at the same time they also erased the cultures that had existed for centuries.

The mission era came to an abrupt end when Mexico won its independence from Spain in 1821 and made efforts to rid itself of its colonial past. In 1834, the Mexican government secularized the missions and evicted the Spanish-born Franciscans and their native converts. Most of the missions were abandoned and, along with their hand-built irrigation works, were left to crumble and deteriorate. But the padres had planted the seeds for the greening of California, and inevitably those ideas would germinate.

That would happen in another century, but only after further changes transformed California. Mexico's brief dominance saw the state sliced up into huge ranchos and the introduction of cattle ranching. Meanwhile, the United States was expanding westward.

Some of the mountain men, trappers and explorers who had pushed their way into the Rocky Mountains, moved on to the Pacific Coast. Once there, some stayed on, settling in California. In the 1840s, conflict with the Mexican government became inevitable as the United States and Mexico vied for dominance over Texas, the southwest and California. The latter fell to the Americans after sporadic skirmishing in 1846 and 1847 when the Mexicans surrendered at Campo de Cahuenga in the San Fernando Valley.

California remained backwater territory until January 1848 when James Marshall discovered gold — the flakes were worth 50 cents apiece — in the tailrace of a lumber mill he was running at Sutter's Fort on the south fork of the American River near Sacramento. Within a year, the California Gold Rush was on, and fortune hunters from all over the world swarmed over the foothills of the Sierra Nevada in Central and Northern California. In a single year the '49ers, as the first big wave of California immigrants were to be remembered, swelled the state's population from 5,000 to 70,000. Initially, Southern California was unaffected by the Gold Rush. In the nearly seven decades since its founding, the population of the

THE REGION'S MILD MEDITERRANEAN CLIMATE INEVITABLY BEGAN LURING SOME OF THE MIGRANTS SOUTHWARD FROM THE GOLD FIELDS.

Gold panning — the dream of riches

Water spun the wheels providing the power for mills.

town of Los Angeles had grown to only about 1,500. But the region's mild Mediterranean climate inevitably began luring some of the migrants southward from the gold fields.

Rain was scarce in the winter of 1862-63. It was the start of a familiar cycle, one that Southern California's Native Americans had learned to expect in earlier centuries. Drought had returned to the region and would provide a cruel reminder that Southern California was a semidesert. The drought would extend for three bitter years, withering the pastures and drying up the springs, streams and watering holes upon which the cattle ranchers relied. Thousands of head of cattle starved or died of thirst as an industry came to an abrupt end. Despite this disaster, the future still seemed limitless for Los Angeles and Southern California. The climate and availability of land were powerful magnets that would continue to attract new citizens. But at some time, the region would have to face the reality of the scarcity of water.

Los Angeles on the move

Chapter 2

THE MULHOLLAND LEGACY

Perhaps the shrewdest investment ever made by the city of Los Angeles came in 1902 when it purchased the private Los Angeles Water Company. For $2 million, the city not only protected its historic source of water, the Los Angeles River, but it also bought the services of the water company's superintendent, William Mulholland.

William Mulholland

Mulholland had held that job for 16 years, but his biggest achievements still lay ahead of him. This flinty-eyed Irishman was a rare visionary. He saw how the future of Los Angeles and all of Southern California was inexorably linked to water and set out to provide the city with a reliable supply. Mulholland was California's first great water bearer and he established a tradition of leadership that would provide the state with a water resources development network in the 20th century that is second to none. "This was the man," wrote water historian Remi Nadeau, "who, Moses-like, was to lead the Angelenos out of the desert." Mulholland's legacy would include the building of one aqueduct system; laying the groundwork for a second, bigger system that the Metropolitan Water District would be created to construct and operate, and the catastrophic St. Francis Dam failure that would hurtle him into retirement in 1928.

Arriving in Los Angeles in the winter of 1877, Mulholland wasn't dreaming of building vast water works. Just 22, with $10 to his name, he was an immigrant who had been roaming the country since he was 17. Born in Belfast, Ireland, he had shipped before the mast out of Liverpool, England, at the early age of 15, and two years later, landed in America full of ambition, enthusiasm, self-confidence and dreams. He had labored on the docks, and he'd worked Great Lakes steamships and Colorado River sidewheelers that hauled supplies to mines and returned laden with ore. For a while, he'd even prospected for gold in Arizona.

Los Angeles' water system had begun to grow and change when Mulholland landed in California. From the beginning, Los Angeles had

Van Nuys ranch in 1898

relied on its namesake river for water. Rude dams had been built and its generally-sparse waters parceled out to fields and homes by open ditches, or *zanjas*, and waterwheels. In 1854, this water system, which by then also included water lines fashioned from hollow logs, had become a city department. By the time Mulholland arrived some 23 years later, the city population of nearly 11,000 could rely on water mains and reservoirs for their supply. And the system by then had been leased to a private firm, the Los Angeles Water Company.

Mulholland wasn't trained as an engineer, and, in fact, in 1878, taking up a pick and shovel, he went to work for the privately-owned crude little city water works as a common laborer — a *zanjero* or ditch tender. Yet, he had a thirst for knowledge and was pragmatic, traits which motivated him to study at night, teaching himself engineering and hydrology.

Eight years later as Los Angeles faced boom times, Mulholland was named superintendent of the company. Competing railroads serving the Southland ignited the real estate market, and by 1892 Los Angeles had more than 50,000 residents and a growing water problem. The city was starting to outstrip its supply of water from the Los Angeles River and countless wells across Southern California had begun to deplete the region's other primary source, groundwater basins. All across Southern California the water table fell as another drought stretched on for eight years.

Under Mulholland's superintendency, Los Angeles began metering water use in an attempt to cut consumption. The meters worked, but it was a losing battle. The city swelled to more than 102,000 residents by the dawn of the new century. Mulholland reckoned that growth would continue and calculated Los Angeles would mushroom to nearly 400,000 by 1925. His forecast was way off the mark. The city exploded to more than a million residents in that span. But Mulholland's judgment that Los Angeles had to begin looking for another source of water had been right on target.

He began that quest in earnest after voters passed a bond issue in 1902 and the city reacquired the then private Los Angeles Water Company and, with it, his services. For the next two years, Mulholland studied the region surrounding Los Angeles. He probed and surveyed the San Gabriel River, the Big Tujunga, the south fork of the Kern River, Piru Creek and the Mojave River. Every river and groundwater basin south of Tehachapi came under his scrutiny before he concluded that none could answer the city's long-term water problem.

Finally, in the summer of 1904, Mulholland approached Fred Eaton, an old friend and former mayor of Los Angeles who had once told him of an

BY THE TIME MULHOLLAND ARRIVED, THE CITY POPULATION OF NEARLY 11,000 COULD RELY ON WATER MAINS AND RESERVOIRS FOR THEIR SUPPLY.

unbelievable source of water on the eastern slope of the Sierra Nevada. In desperation, Mulholland asked him to "show me this water supply." More than a decade before, Eaton had come across the Owens Valley on the eastern flank of the Sierra Nevada, some 200 miles north of Los Angeles. The valley was rich in water. For more than 150 miles a network of creeks and streams funneled the snowmelt of the Sierra into the Owens River which filled Owens Lake, an alkaline dead sea at the lower end of the valley. Eaton also had worked for the Los Angeles Water Company and saw that the lake had been created by a recent — in geologic terms — lava flow. Before that, the Owens River had coursed to the south, straight for the mountains on the northern rim of Los Angeles. Mulholland hadn't been interested in this distant river, but now with his city running out of options and water, he was ready to listen to Eaton.

Fred Eaton

In July, the two men headed north in an old buckboard pulled by a team of mules. Eaton was confident the Owens River was the answer to Los Angeles' problems. His belief was borne out when the pair arrived in the valley and Mulholland saw for the first time the abundance of water coming off the mountains. There was enough available, Mulholland figured, for 2 million people. In the days that followed, he and Eaton explored the valley and a possible route for bringing water to Los Angeles. Mulholland soon became a believer. Here was a plentiful source of water for his adopted city, and it could be imported more than 200 miles entirely by gravity. No pumping would be required.

Mulholland and Eaton returned to Los Angeles to sell their vision and Mulholland's engineering recommendations to the city. It was an easy task and in 1905 voters, by a margin of 14-to-1, supported a $1.5 million bond issue to purchase land in the Owens Valley and begin preliminary work on what was to be called the Los Angeles Aqueduct.

Eaton headed back to the Owens Valley to secure water rights and land purchase options for the city. The entrepreneurial Eaton was successful, but he also sowed the seeds of mistrust, suspicion and controversy, which have plagued the aqueduct system for nearly eight decades. Los Angeles wasn't the only government entity looking at the Owens Valley in the early 1900s. The fledgling U.S. Reclamation Service also was interested in the region for a potential project. Eaton was aware of the Reclamation Service's plans and as he went about his work for the city he also was employed by the federal agency to investigate several private applications to develop power projects in the valley. Inevitably, his dual role led to charges of misrepresentation. Some of the people from whom Eaton purchased land or water rights later claimed they were deceived, believing they were selling to the federal government and not Los Angeles.

Surveying the route to bring water to a growing Los Angeles

The future of the Owens Valley reached all the way to Washington, D.C. and the White House, when in 1906, the city sought a right of way across federal land to build the Los Angeles Aqueduct. California Senator Frank Flint introduced a bill granting those rights, and it sailed through the upper chamber. However, Congressman Sylvester Smith of Inyo County organized opposition to the proposal in the House of Representatives where it became stalled. While Smith was fighting his holding action, Flint took the dispute to President Theodore Roosevelt. The president, after meeting with Flint, Secretary of the Interior Ethan Hitchcock, Chief of Forest Service Gifford Pinchot and other advisors, came out strongly for Los Angeles. In a letter, Roosevelt wrote, "...yet it is a hundred or a thousand fold more important to the state and more valuable to the people as a whole if [the water and power resources were] used by the city than if used by the people of the Owens Valley." Five days later the House of Representatives passed Senator Flint's bill and Los Angeles had a green light to build Mulholland's aqueduct. One year later, Los Angeles voters approved a second bond issue, providing $23 million to construct the 223-mile system.

Work began in the fall of 1908 on what was then the biggest aqueduct in the world. The scale of the job that Mulholland had planned was awesome. More than 1,000 miles of roads, pipeline, power transmission lines and telephone and telegraph lines were built and strung to support and supply the main construction effort. The Southern Pacific Railroad was convinced that it should build a new track from Mojave north to Lone Pine in the Owens Valley with the promise of having an estimated 14 million tons of freight to haul over the line. Fifty-seven work camps were erected along the route of the aqueduct to house and feed the army of men who were to build it.

Construction of the Los Angeles Aqueduct from the eastern Sierra

The Los Angeles Aqueduct was built with the assistance of power shovels and dredges, mule teams and air hammers. But its primary ingredients were blasting powder and concrete — and the toil and sweat of a huge labor force. The men came from throughout the country, indeed from around the world, to work for wages ranging from $2.25 a day for a laborer to $3 for an experienced miner.

Veteran miners and tough construction workers joined the department's professionals to lead the way. But much of the brawn was supplied by immigrant laborers from such places as Greece, Bulgaria, Serbia, Montenegro, Mexico and Switzerland, who worked long and hard, saving their wages for the day they could return to their homelands. Many were men who could neither read nor write English, but painstakingly learned to scrawl their signatures so they could cash their paychecks. They toiled alongside Americans known as "bindle stiffs," who got this name from a habit of carrying their bindles, or bedding, on their backs as they drifted from one job to another. A colorful lot, they never stayed in one place very long and talked little about their past lives, many revealing no more than a nickname.

Turnover among the workers was high. Even though Mulholland's payroll never exceeded 3,900 men at any time, an estimated 100,000 had a hand in building the aqueduct by the time it was finished in 1913. While the work was hard and dirty and conditions were difficult, workers were

Mules haul 36-ton siphon sections.

ITS PRIMARY INGREDIENTS WERE BLASTING POWDER AND CONCRETE — AND THE TOIL AND SWEAT OF A HUGE LABOR FORCE.

RESIDENTS TURNED OUT EN MASSE ON NOVEMBER 5, 1913, TO SEE THE FIRST WATER FROM THE OWENS VALLEY TUMBLE DOWN THE "CASCADES" INTO THE NORTHERN SAN FERNANDO VALLEY.

Mulholland opens LA Aqueduct: "There it is. Take it."

provided shelter, food and, surprisingly for the time, a medical department to see to the needs of those employed in the construction of the Los Angeles Aqueduct.

Six million pounds of explosives were consumed by this work force in the process of opening 142 tunnels that stretched for more than 43 miles. Concrete was used so extensively that decades later someone calculated a road 12 feet wide and 6 inches thick from Portland, Oregon, to Yuma, Arizona, might have been constructed from the stuff. To make sure it had enough raw materials, the city bought more than 4,000 acres of land in the foothills of the Mojave Desert near the town of Monolith. There, feeding off deposits of clay and limestone, a mill churned out 1,000 barrels of Portland cement a day.

The use of steel pipe was restricted because of high transportation costs: It was manufactured on the Atlantic Coast and shipped around Cape Horn in those pre-Panama Canal days. Still, it was essential in some locations and the construction of 12 miles of steel siphons was among the greatest engineering challenges of the entire aqueduct project. These siphons spanned rugged mountain and desert canyons, perhaps the most imposing of which was an 8,095-foot-long siphon across forbidding Jawbone Canyon. Ranging from 7.5 to 10 feet in diameter, this siphon drops 850 feet to the bottom of the canyon before looping up to the northern rim and weighs more than 3,200 tons.

From the start of the project, Mulholland realized that finishing the aqueduct on time would depend upon being able to "hole out" the five-mile Elizabeth Tunnel, the longest on the system. The job of driving the tunnel, which a board of engineers had estimated would take five years to carve out, began concurrently with the start of work on the roads, power lines and other support projects. Mulholland's miners were more than equal to the task, finishing the job 20 months ahead of schedule. Crews were spurred on by bonuses offered for increased production and competition with miners working on other projects. The Elizabeth Tunnel crew raced and beat miners digging the Gunnison Tunnel in Colorado. The Red Rock Tunnel crew raced a Swiss crew digging a tunnel for a railroad line through the Bernaise Alps and set a world record as a result.

Such successful performances enabled the Los Angeles Aqueduct to be completed on schedule, and residents turned out en masse on November 5,1913, to see the first water from the Owens Valley tumble down the "Cascades" into the northern San Fernando Valley. More than 30,000 onlookers turned out for what the Los Angeles Times described as "the biggest and most heartfelt celebration ever held in Los Angeles. By automobile and train, people poured through the various thoroughfares to the amphitheater at the foot of the Cascades."

It was a day of triumph for Mulholland and as the water thundered into the San Fernando Valley, he uttered his famous five-word speech: "There it is. Take it."

Completion of the Los Angeles Aqueduct signaled a pause rather than a

Mulholland sets off in search of a route from the Colorado.

final solution to Southern California's long-term water problems. It was an interlude that spanned less than a decade.

The region's population continued to expand at a rate that outstripped earlier projections. By the 1920s, there were almost 1 million Angelenos, and surrounding communities such as Pasadena, Santa Monica, Anaheim, Long Beach, Santa Ana, Burbank and Glendale were growing as well. In addition, Southern California was becoming an industrial center and its agricultural base continued to grow, putting more pressure on water supplies. Then, in the early 1920s another paralyzing drought afflicted California. Once again Southern California resumed its quest.

This search would extend eastward toward the Colorado River; once more Bill Mulholland would be in the vanguard. On October 29, 1923, Mulholland launched the first survey for a possible aqueduct route. He and a small group of companions set a boat in the Colorado River near Boulder Canyon and in four days rowed and floated downstream to Parker, Arizona. But this time, the job would be too big for one man and one city to tackle. Southern Californians would band together to create a new agency, the Metropolitan Water District, to build the largest water project the world had ever seen. And in the process, one of America's wildest rivers, the Colorado, would have to be tamed.

Chapter 3

THE RIVER

The unruly Colorado

Now Mulholland had his eye fixed on the Colorado, a raging, unruly brute of a river that hid its mysterious course in cavernous abysses for nearly a thousand miles, reluctantly revealing it only to the brave and hardy. For more than three centuries, the Colorado stubbornly resisted the efforts of conquistadors, Jesuit and Franciscan priests, fur trappers, army expeditions, Mormon settlers and others. It was only with the greatest of human daring and hardship that the river had been forced to yield the final secrets of its route to John Wesley Powell, a one-armed soldier-scientist who had come upon the scene a scant five decades before Mulholland proposed to harness the river.

The Colorado and its tributaries make up one of the great river systems of North America, forming a network of waterways that reaches into seven states and drains an area just shy of a quarter of a million square miles. Its exact point of origin can't be fixed with certainty, but its meager beginnings are somewhere 14,000 feet above sea level in the Never Summer

Mountain Range on the western edge of Rocky Mountain National Park in northern Colorado. From there innumerable trickles, rills, creeks, streams and rivers join together on a twisting 1,700-mile journey to the southwest that ends in Mexico as the Colorado spills into the Gulf of California.

The spectacular course of the river has evolved over its estimated 12-million-year lifetime. A mighty mover of soil and stone, winning its name from the reddish burden of earth its waters carried, the Colorado, ever so slowly, but persistently, sliced its way through the rocky mantle covering the plateaus of the southwest. It carved out awesome works, the most extraordinary being Arizona's Grand Canyon, truly one of the earth's great natural wonders. Here massive rock formations, taking on the ambience of a cathedral, attest to the power and sculptural grace of water. Relentlessly, the Colorado also revealed a rainbow of sandstone, shale, limestone, granite and schist layers, exposing a mile-deep natural "mural" dating back 2 billion years.

The first known humans to visit the Grand Canyon go back just 4,000 years. This is the date ascribed by archaeologists to split-willow figures left in caves along the canyon bottom by prehistoric Indian hunters. Little is known about these first river people and they are believed to have disappeared from the area by the beginning of the Christian era. Soon after, around 400 A.D., Pueblo peoples, ancestors of today's Hopi, occupied the region, leaving evidence of their having explored the canyon by the year 700. Other tribes — the Sinagua, Cohoninas, Havasupai and Walapai — followed them into the area. Upriver, along the Colorado, its tributary the Green and subsidiary streams, lived the Fremont peoples. Beginning around 700 A.D., they inhabited the region for about 500 years before they moved on. By 1500, Ute and Paiutes had moved into the territory that soon would be exposed to European adventurers.

Within 40 years of Columbus' discovery of the New World, the Spanish

Nature's wonder — the Grand Canyon

INNUMERABLE TRICKLES, RILLS, CREEKS, STREAMS AND RIVERS JOIN TOGETHER ON A TWISTING 1,700-MILE JOURNEY TO THE SOUTHWEST.

Spanish explorers

had boldly marched into the Americas and wrested vast treasures from its Indian inhabitants. Hernando Cortez had seized the booty of Mexico's Aztec Empire in 1521. Eleven years later, Francisco Pizarro conquered Peru's Incas, capturing their gold, silver and jewels for the Spanish crown. It is no wonder then, that other Spaniards believed rumors and legends of the fabled Seven Cities of Cibola, seven golden cities, somewhere to the north of the newly conquered Aztecs. In fact, the Spanish explorer-priest Fray Marcos de Niza even claimed he had seen one of these cities and that it was bigger and grander than any in Mexico. What he had really seen, and only from a distance, was a modest Zuni settlement in the western portion of present-day New Mexico.

In 1540, Antonio de Mendoza, the viceroy of Mexico, launched a two-pronged expedition into the area that would become the American Southwest to search for the seven golden cities. Hernando de Alarcon commanded the naval arm of the expedition and was sent with three ships to sail up the Sea of Cortez (Gulf of California). Eventually, according to Mendoza's plan, carrying supplies, Alarcon's force would make contact with the land expedition consisting of 230 caballeros, numerous footmen, five friars, a military escort, nearly a thousand native American servants and more than 1500 horses, mules and beef cattle—all under the command of Francisco Vasquez de Coronado. The Spanish, blinded by the promise of another treasure trove, were woefully ignorant of the geography, and their forces never met. Independently, however, both Coronado and Alarcon discovered the Colorado River.

By land, Coronado's force marched more than 1,000 miles and by early July approached the first of the seven golden cities, the crowded, squalid, Zuni village, quite devoid of valuables, seen by Fray Marcos. Alarcon, meanwhile, set sail for his rendezvous. In August, he reached what he later called in his official report "a mighty river, which ran with so great fury of a storm, that we could hardly sail against it." He had discovered the mouth of the Colorado and found navigating upstream difficult. Ever resourceful, Alarcon bartered beads and trinkets with the local Cocopah Indians who towed his three ships up the Colorado into southern Arizona as far as its confluence with the Gila River. There, Alarcon heard stories from other Indians of white men in the land to the east. The Spanish commander continued up the river for another hundred or so miles. By the end of summer, Alarcon still had not made contact, so he reversed his course, sailing downriver and back into the Gulf of California.

During this time Coronado was not idle. In the Zuni village he had captured, the conquistador heard tales of a great river somewhere to the west that was inhabited by a race of giants. Coronado sent Don Garcia Lopez de Cardenas and a dozen men to explore that land. They moved deep into land that would become Arizona, eventually reaching the south rim of the Grand Canyon. They, too, had discovered the yet unnamed Colorado, but cursed the river and the splendor it had created. To Cardenas, the river and the canyon were impenetrable barriers blocking the path to the seven cities of gold that lay somewhere ahead over the distant horizon. It was "a useless piece of country" he wrote to Coronado.

So Coronado turned east and north in his epic, but fruitless, wandering journey across a vast expanse of North America. Cardenas' "useless" label stuck and the Colorado and the southwest were ignored for nearly 100 years. This period of neglect ended in the 17th century with the arrival of the Black Robes, Jesuit priests who came to the New World in search of souls to save. More than 3,000 Jesuits worked to convert the native population of New Spain, as the vast Spanish holdings in Mexico and the United States were called. A handful of these men were instrumental in opening the Southwest for settlement and the Colorado River for renewed exploration. Foremost among them was Fray Eusebio Francisco Kino. His maps and accounts from the 1690s and early 1700s were instrumental in convincing Spain of the importance of the Colorado River. Kino also believed that California was not an island, though that was the prevailing view of the time. In 1701, he set out from his mission base in Sonora, Mexico, to find a land route to California. The map Kino drafted in 1705 found its way to Europe and carried a new name, the Colorado River.

Kino's overland route to California eventually was secured, in time to help maintain the infant missions and pueblos that Spain began establishing in 1769. In 1774, Juan Bautista de Anza led an overland expedition to the San Fernando Valley. The following year he returned again, this time to Northern California to colonize what was to become San Francisco. There also was a new order of priests, the Franciscans. The Black Robes had opened up much unknown country in the New World, but politics had taken its toll and they had been banished from New Spain in 1767. The Franciscans, less militant, but no less dedicated, took up where the Jesuits left off.

In July of 1776, two Franciscans, Fray Francisco Atanasio Dominguez and Fray Silvestre de Escalante, departed Santa Fe on a 2,000-mile journey through the wilds of Ute country, hoping to blaze a trail from New Mexico to Monterey, California, that would avoid the region's canyon country. However, they never made it to their destination. The two padres were thwarted from reaching the Pacific Coast by snow storms near the site of what is today St. George, Utah. Still Escalante and Dominguez were the first to explore and chart vast regions of the Southwest, and they uncovered a crossing point along the Colorado, just east of the spot in Arizona later to be dubbed Lee Ferry. They also discovered large stretches of what soon would become the Old Spanish Trail, a route from Santa Fe to California following the path of least geographic resistance through Utah that would be used for three-quarters of a century.

Another Franciscan, Padre Francisco Garces, labored for more than a dozen years to establish a mission along the lower Colorado, only to be clubbed to death in 1781 by Yuma warriors during an Indian revolt. This uprising shut down the overland routes to California and drew a curtain on more than two centuries of Spanish efforts to explore the Colorado

Mountain men opened up the Green and the upper reaches of the Colorado.

River and the Southwest. Soon, however, pioneers of the newly formed United States would begin their westward push across the continent and once again the Colorado would become the focus of attention.

In the vanguard of this new and final wave of exploration were the mountain men and fur trappers of the 1820s who made their tortuous way through the Rocky Mountains. It was the American fur trade and the pursuit of beaver pelts that first opened the West and led to the final exploration of the Colorado. Rivers and streams were the highways of these adventurers and the source of the furs they sought. It was in the vicinity of the upper reaches of the Green River that the mountain men gathered year after year to conduct the commerce of their trade.

Inevitably, the mountain men headed down the Green to the Colorado. William Ashley, former judge, munitions maker, real estate speculator and lieutenant governor of Missouri turned trapper-trader, was one of the first. In 1825, he probed the canyons and rapids of the Green River getting as far as a place called Desolation Canyon. In the years ahead, Ashley hired other adventuresome men to work for him and go ever deeper into the wilderness.

The Army dispatched expeditions into the canyon country and deserts after the Mexican War to survey wagon roads, pacify hostile Indians and find possible routes for the proposed transcontinental railroad. At the same time, the California gold rush sent thousands of would-be prospec-

One of the last of the steamboats to ply the Colorado out of Yuma

tors streaming across the continent only to bump against the barrier presented by the Colorado River. A ferry crossing was established near Yuma, but the hordes of '49ers provoked local Indians and the army had to step in to provide protection. In 1850, Fort Yuma was built on a bluff overlooking the point where the Gila River emptied into the Colorado. Soon after, a second redoubt, Fort Mojave, was constructed 200 miles upstream.

To supply these remote desert outposts, the Army eventually decided to rely on steamboats. The pioneering steamboat captain on the river was George Johnson, who built his first vessel, the Yuma, in 1851. Johnson used it to haul supplies to the forts from a ship anchored in the Gulf of California. He soon became interested in exploring farther up the Colorado, but promised government funds were diverted to another man, Lt. Joseph Christmas Ives of the U.S. Army Topographical Engineers. Ives was given the job of opening up the Colorado and exploring the unknown reaches of the river's canyons. He was to be provided a 58-foot, steel-hulled steamboat to accomplish his assignment. But first the vessel, which was built in Philadelphia, had to be dismantled, shipped around South America and reassembled at the mouth of the Colorado. He was ready to steam upriver in January 1858, but an angry Johnson beat him to the punch. With one of his own steamers, Johnson chugged as far north as El Dorado Canyon. Ives, not to be outdone, was able to navigate another 30 miles upriver, as far north as Black Canyon, the site where Hoover Dam would one day be built.

Members of the Ives expedition left their steamer at that point and continued on foot. Nine days later, they became the first white men to explore the floor of the Grand Canyon. But like Cardenas more than three centuries earlier, Ives wasn't impressed. To his Army superiors he wrote: "Ours has been the first and will doubtless be the last party of whites to visit this profitless locality. It seems intended by nature that the Colorado River, along the greater portion of its lonely and majestic way, shall be forever unvisited and undisturbed."

Ives was a poor prophet. Just 11 years later another soldier would conquer the river and unlock its final secrets. This was John Wesley Powell, an inquisitive, driving man with a fascination for natural history. Powell had been a farmer, school principal, field scientist, explorer, public servant and a major in the Union Army, where he had lost his right arm on the battlefield of Shiloh. He also was a skilled organizer, promoter and strong leader.

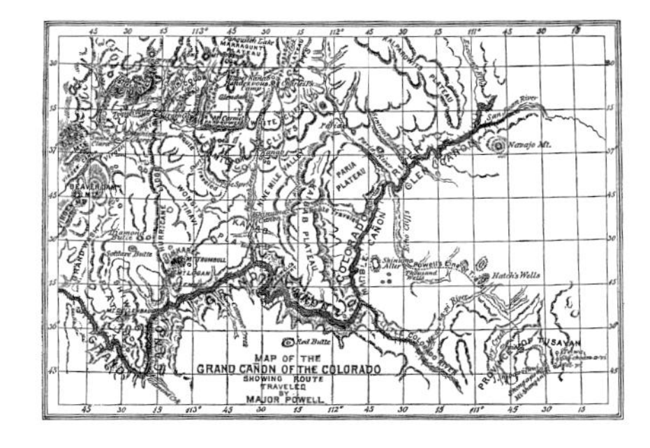

Powell's map of the Colorado

Powell built on the pioneering exploration of the Mormons who were attempting to colonize the forbidding and rugged canyon country of the Colorado in the 1850s and '60s. At the close of the Civil War, Powell made two trips to the Colorado Rockies. There he explored the high country and the headwaters of the river and its tributaries. It was on these journeys that Powell began formulating his grand dream. Other explorers and army expeditions had visited various reaches of the Colorado. But some segments of the river still had not been seen by any other than Native Americans and no one had traversed the length of the river. Powell wanted to be the man who accomplished that feat.

On May 24, 1869, he set out on the first of several epic river journeys with 10 men and four specially constructed boats. Powell planned to run Wyoming's Green River to its confluence with the Grand where the two streams met to form the Colorado and then down the main stem of the river through the Grand Canyon. It was a pioneering voyage into the unknown because Powell had neither maps nor reports to guide him. His companions were an odd lot. He had recruited trappers, Army men, a printer, a boatman, a bullwhacker and an adventuresome Englishman. Only Powell and six of his men would complete the trip. The Englishman became disillusioned quickly and quit. Three others deserted the expedition in the Grand Canyon just two days before the journey's end, fearing the rapids that lay ahead. They managed to scramble to the top of the canyon and head for Mormon settlements in southern Utah. They never reached them, for they were killed three days later by Shivwits Paiutes who mistook them for prospectors who had ravaged a squaw.

Black Canyon

The going was harrowing for the expedition. Powell lost one of his boats and some of his rations in the first rapids. A second had to be left in the canyon after the trio deserted. It had taken six weeks to reach the Grand Canyon and then another seven to navigate its turbulent and treacherous rapids, whirlpools and eddies. Split-second, life-or-death decisions had become commonplace. With food scarce, water-logged and turning moldy, Powell and six tired men emerged from the canyon on August 30. At the confluence of the Virgin and Colorado rivers, they encountered a party of Mormons dragging the waters with nets for their remains. Powell and his men had been reported drowned, and Brigham Young had asked his people to search for any trace of them.

The one-armed explorer was an instant hero. He traveled to Washington where he secured $10,000 from Congress for a second journey down the river. These two trips were but the beginning of Powell's efforts to understand the river and its vast canyons. Through the 1870s, he studied both the terrain and its people and prepared geological maps that more that a century later remain classical cartography. Ultimately, Powell concluded that the Colorado was absolutely unsuitable for navigation above Black Canyon. The Army refused to accept his conclusion and attempted to

John Wesley Powell

send one more expedition upstream from Fort Mojave. It was a total failure. The Colorado proved too powerful and dangerous for navigation in its upper reaches.

At nearly the same time, other men already were dreaming of harnessing the Colorado for irrigation. As early as 1860, Dr. Oliver Wozencraft and San Diego County surveyor Eb Hadley proposed using water from the Colorado to irrigate and colonize 3 million acres in California's Imperial Valley. Sixteen years later, the U.S. Army Corps of Engineers sent Lt. Eric Bergland to conduct surveys. Bergland's goal was to find a route for the canal that was entirely within the United States. But Bergland, and others who followed him, all concluded that any canal would have to partially pass through Mexico where a natural route was available. After several unsuccessful attempts to develop these lands, finally in 1901 the private California Development Company under the leadership of promoter Charles Rockwood and engineer George Chaffey constructed the Alamo Canal. A 50-mile stretch crossed Mexico, leaving the valley farmers at the mercy of a foreign government — a situation that would be corrected some 30 years later.

The canal opened the fertile fields of the Imperial Valley to agriculture. But it was a time bomb. Within three years, tons of sand silted up a four-mile stretch. The near-bankrupt California Development Company, fearing ruin if it couldn't supply the 100,000 Imperial Valley acres they had under contract with river water, cut a new 60-foot-gash in the bank of the Colorado just across the border into Mexico — despite the fact that it had no funds with which to build a control gate.

1904 Colorado River flood

But nature was not on its side. In 1904, heavy spring floods roared through the new breach in the river, widening it and inundating farmland as far as the eye could see. Efforts to fill the widening break were foiled by ongoing floods which climaxed in November when a torrent thundered down to the Colorado from its Gila River tributary. The entire Colorado River swept through the cut, coursed downhill across the desert (digging the great gash which is now the New River) and raced north into the Salton Sink, 300 feet below sea level, where midday brought temperatures of 120 degrees and higher. And thus the Salton Sink became the Salton Sea. It took nearly two years to stem the flow and confine the river to its original course.

This then was the river that Mulholland proposed to tap for Southern California. It was unnavigable, unruly and, perhaps worst of all, its waters became a roiling maelstrom of political contention.

Chapter 4

THE POLITICS OF WATER

The Colorado

In the arid west, water was power, wealth and life. Both a commodity and essential resource, it pitted seven western states against each other, as well as the combined interests of some of those states against those of Mexico. The Colorado was a river that provoked harsh rhetoric, even fighting words; at one juncture Arizona was prepared to go to war with California to protect its claims. At times, finding a route and building the Colorado River Aqueduct would seem modest tasks compared with the protracted political and legal wars over the waters of the river. The struggle to adjudicate the water rights of the Colorado is almost as old as the 20th century and one that has yet to be completely resolved. The United States Supreme Court still has pending before it several Indian reservation claims involving water rights along the lower Colorado.

At the heart of this long debate is title to the use of the waters of a powerful river. Despite its 1,700-mile course and the awesome geologic monuments it has created, the Colorado's resources are limited. Its flow is driven by the weather. Before being tamed by man, heavy rains or sudden desert flash floods could unleash unbelievably powerful rushes of water capable of sweeping away everything in their paths, while dry or drought years, which can appear at any time and over which man has no control, would shrink the river dramatically. In an average year, the Colorado actually carries less water than California's Sacramento River. Just how much water the Colorado contains has been a subject of debate. Records of its volume in the 20th century suggest its average annual runoff is between 14 and 15 million acre-feet. However, tree ring research paints a drier picture, though the accuracy of this type of research is yet to be proven. The climate in the river basin dating back to the 15th century was reconstructed based on data stored in the annual growth rings of trees. The results indicate the average runoff annually may have been in the neighborhood of only 13.5 million acre-feet.

Indeed, the Colorado had time and again proved itself wild and

ATER LAW IN MOST WESTERN STATES WAS BASED ON THE BASIC PRINCIPLE THAT WHOEVER FIRST USED THE WATER HAD THE FIRST CLAIM OR RIGHT TO THE WATER.

tumultuous. Finally, in the wake of the disastrous 1904 flood that had created the Salton Sea, residents along the lower Colorado River and in Imperial Valley began demanding permanent flood control works on the river. At the same time, Imperial Valley farmers still called for an irrigation canal that didn't cross Mexico, a so-called "All-American Canal." Half of the flow in the existing Alamo Canal was guaranteed to Mexico and agriculture was expanding quickly south of the border in the Colorado River delta. Arizona added its voice to the cry for flood control after Yuma was flooded in 1916.

The Imperial Irrigation District, which had assumed operation of the Imperial Canal in 1911, spearheaded efforts for federal involvement in both flood control works and an All-American Canal. IID, under the leadership of Phil Swing, its attorney who was later to become a congressman, and Mark Rose, a crusty farmer, worked to win the support of the federal Bureau of Reclamation. In June 1919, a bureau engineering board recommended building the canal and, significantly, added that the U.S. government also "should undertake the early construction of a storage reservoir on the drainage basin of the Colorado."

While this report was greeted with enthusiasm by people along the river's lower stretches, it was viewed with alarm in the upper basin states. Building a reservoir would ultimately result in greater water use and Colorado, Utah, Wyoming and New Mexico were worried about the fast-growing lower basin states. They feared California and Arizona would establish prior rights to large amounts of the river's water before they could make use of flows passing through the upper basin. Water law in most western states was based on the basic principle that whoever first used the water had the first claim or right to the water. The United States Supreme Court extended this so-called "first in time, first in right" rule across state boundaries in its 1921 decision in the case of *Wyoming vs. Colorado.*

From 1918 to 1921, the seven river states fruitlessly attempted to resolve

Colorado River basin states

their differences. Each state sought to establish its own limits on how much Colorado River water it would use. At the same time, the three lower basin states, particularly California, demanded that a dam be built to provide flood control. The upper basin states pledged to block such a proposal in Congress until each state established reasonable limits on its demands for river water. This deadlock stretched into 1922, months after the Colorado River Commission was established with delegates from the seven basin states. With Secretary of Commerce Herbert Hoover representing the federal government, nine meetings of the commission failed to solve the dispute. Finally, a 15-day session broke the impasse.

The climatic meetings resulted in the drafting of a flawed and incomplete document — or so many believe — termed the Colorado River Compact. The compact was hammered out at about the same time that the House of Representatives began considering a bill to construct a dam at Black Canyon, near Boulder Canyon, introduced by the Imperial Valley's new congressman, Phil Swing. Introduction of the Boulder Dam bill prodded the upper basin states to seek some sort of accommodation to protect their future water rights.

The Colorado River Compact did that by dividing the river into upper and lower basins at Lee Ferry in Arizona, downstream from the Utah-Arizona border, and allocating the right to use 7.5 million acre-feet of water annually to each basin. The states in each basin were then responsible for dividing the use of the apportioned water among themselves. Moreover, water stored in the upper basin that was not put to beneficial use had to remain available for use by lower basin states.

The Colorado River Compact was signed on November 24, 1922, but the squabbling among the basin states was far from over.

The compact, however, totally ignored the issues of constructing a huge storage dam to provide flood control and of building an all-American canal. The compact also contained one other thorny provision. As a compromise between the position held by upper basin states and the insistence of the Arizona delegation, the lower basin was to be allowed to increase its use of water by 1 million acre-feet per year. The Colorado River Compact was signed on November 24, 1922, but the squabbling among the basin states was far from over. The controversy would shift next to the halls of Congress and eventually to the chambers of the Supreme Court.

Authorization of what became known as the Boulder Canyon Project Act turned into a protracted seven-year marathon: the act not only would provide for construction of a major dam across the river, but would approve the compact as well. Only through the persistence of Swing and California Senator Hiram Johnson did the measure finally win Congressional approval. The two Californians introduced authorizing legislation three times and were turned back as the seven basin states continued to bicker over the Colorado despite the compact they had signed. A fourth attempt was successful in 1928, notwithstanding considerable debate in the Senate, an Arizona filibuster and survival of a joint resolution providing for a thorough investigation of the economic and engineering features of the project.

The biggest obstacle to hurdle was Arizona. The legislatures of six basin states had ratified the Colorado River Compact by early 1923. But

oulder Canyon

Arizona stubbornly refused. And without ratification by all seven states, the compact would be void, negating the possibility of Congress casting a favorable vote on the Boulder Canyon Project. Two years later, in 1925, a new bill requiring ratification of the compact by just six states was drafted. The four upper basin states and Nevada rushed to approve it. California moved to cast the sixth vote, but the state Legislature attached what became known as the Finney Resolution to its ratification. This amendment linked California's vote to Congressional approval of a 20-million-acre-foot reservoir near Boulder Canyon. The upper basin states refused to accept this linkage and blocked the attempt by Swing and Johnson to steer a Boulder Canyon Project bill through Congress.

California remained firm, refusing to repeal the Finney Resolution, and in late 1926 the upper states amended a third Swing-Johnson bill to protect their interests. Then with compromise and passage possible, the Utah Legislature backtracked and repealed its Colorado River Compact ratification. A subsequent bill introduced in 1927 was filibustered into defeat by Arizona. But California was making headway and the Swing-Johnson team once more sought legislative approval in the second 1928 session. The key to its success was quashing another Arizona filibuster and California's agreeing to a limitation on its share of the water use allocated to the lower basin by the Colorado River Compact. Finally, on December 14, 1928, the United States Senate voted "aye" on the Boulder Canyon Project Act. The House followed within days and on December 21,

The first Metropolitan Water District board of directors

President Calvin Coolidge signed the measure into law to become effective the following June.

At that time, California restricted itself to 4.4 million acre-feet of the lower basin's 7.5-million-acre-foot use allocation, plus one half of any surplus. Arizona stubbornly refused to concede defeat and in October 1930, petitioned the Supreme Court to declare the Boulder Canyon Project Act unconstitutional. The following May, the court threw out the complaint.

While the Boulder Canyon story was unfolding in Washington, a lesser drama was unfolding in Sacramento, one that would lead to the formation of the Metropolitan Water District of Southern California. William Mulholland's initial Colorado River survey in 1923 aroused the interest of other Southern California cities in this potential source of water and power. The scope of a Colorado River project was believed to be beyond the means of any individual city, and for cities to work cooperatively some form of special district would have to be formed.

Necessary legislation was introduced in the state Senate on January 19, 1925. It called for the organization of metropolitan water districts, and three months later the Senate approved the bill by a vote of 25-to-9. Within a week, however, the state Assembly rejected the measure, 43-32. The aqueduct proposal had wide popular support, nevertheless, and many of the legislators who had voted against the bill were voted out of office in the next election. Enabling legislation was reintroduced in January 1927 and this time there was little opposition. The Senate voted unanimously in favor, 27-0, while the final tally in the Assembly was an overwhelming 63-2.

It was 1928 when voters in 11 cities — Los Angeles, Pasadena, Burbank, Glendale, Beverly Hills, San Marino, Santa Monica, Anaheim, Colton, Santa Ana and San Bernardino — cast ballots in favor of joining the Metropolitan Water District of Southern California. Residents of the cities of Glendora and Orange vetoed the prospect. On December 6, 1928, Metropolitan was incorporated and a short three weeks later, on December 29, after official representatives had been appointed by the member cities, the board of directors convened in Pasadena's Huntington Hotel for the first time to file incorporation papers. Permanent organization followed on February 9, 1929, with W.P. Whitsett, Los Angeles land developer and founder of the town of Van Nuys, elected chairman of the board of directors. Metropolitan's membership would change slightly in the next two years. In early 1931, four other communities — Fullerton, Long Beach, Torrance and Compton — were annexed and two original members — Colton and San Bernardino — withdrew. Banded together, these 13 cities faced a massive job: they had to complete surveys for an aqueduct route, build that 242-mile aqueduct and construct a vast distribution system to bring water from the Colorado to Southern California.

Chapter 5

PICKING THE ROUTE

Surveyors tackle the desert.

Bill Mulholland (standing, wearing vest) and survey party

Targeting the Colorado River as a source of water for Southern California was one thing. Finding the best route for an aqueduct was another. Unlike the Owens River, which had an ancient riverbed pointed toward Los Angeles, there was no direct or easy path over which to bring water from the Colorado to Southern California. The search for the most practical and economical route would span seven years and involve one of the most comprehensive surveying efforts in history. It was a search punctuated by a spirited debate over the kind of aqueduct to build. One side called for an all-gravity system similar to the Los Angeles Aqueduct; the other maintained the best route could be found if pumps were used to lift water over the mountains which separated the river and coastal Southern California.

It took hundreds of men to survey a vast expanse of desert, mountain and canyon country. In all, they charted more than 60,000 square miles of some of the loneliest and most desolate real estate in the United States. Most of it they covered on foot. The surveyors employed first worked under the banner of the city of Los Angeles and later the new Metropolitan Water District. Their search for the safest, most economical route took them to thousands of nameless places in the Southwest. With their transits, rods and chains, the surveyors traveled northeast into Utah and the mouth of the San Juan River. To the south, they went to the Mexican border, explored a corner of Baja California and then, swinging west, followed the boundary to the Pacific Ocean. Even the dizzying geography of the Grand Canyon was mapped as almost every conceivable route was explored.

Ultimately, more than 100 different variations had been pursued before one was endorsed in 1931 — and that one would be the Parker route. It originated along the river within several miles of the spot where Bill Mulholland's first survey party had completed its brief scouting mission in 1923. That may have been coincidence or, perhaps, it may attest to Mulholland's intuition and shrewdness. With the passage of time, some of Mulholland's achievements have assumed near-legendary proportions. He undoubtedly had uncanny foresight; some who worked with him in the survey era, in fact, believed he had chosen the Parker route from the beginning.

"His mind was made up for the Parker route very early. Mulholland was an intuitive genius who could visualize things that others couldn't," said Andrew Gram, the first executive secretary of Metropolitan's board of directors.

"He picked that route way back when the surveying started," added Ray Witt, who joined the surveyors in 1928, "and it was the same as the final one all the way from Parker to Mt. San Jacinto."

Plotting the aqueduct's route: (top) using transit and (bottom) atop marker, holding target

Ferry near Parker carries city of LA survey party across the Colorado.

Nevertheless, before the route was finally selected, it would take more than the instincts of Mulholland to chart the exact course for this new aqueduct. The massive surveying job began in earnest following the passage of a $2 million bond issue by Los Angeles voters in June 1925. It was grueling, painstakingly slow work across a landscape almost entirely devoid of roads. In the early days of the surveys, mule pack trains were sometimes used to haul water, food and equipment. In the instances when they were working along the Colorado, or one of its tributaries, boats were employed. And then, in the later stages of the surveys, Ford Model-T and Model-A station wagons began appearing on the desert and the foot-weary men drove them nearly everywhere over the largely roadless terrain they were roaming. But mostly they walked, packing everything they needed on their backs.

The rewards for scouting places such as the Dead Mountains, Chuckawalla Valley, Black Mesa Springs, Bagdad, Laguna Salada, Old Woman Mountain, Devil's Elbow, Music Mountain and Deadman Point were modest. When Metropolitan took charge of the surveys in May 1930, men were making $90 a month plus room and board. Usually that meant a meal cooked over an open fire and a bedroll spread out in a pup tent that was pitched in the sand or dirt. These "fly camps" — short for fly-by-night camps — were moved almost daily. Occasionally bigger camps, complete with cooks, were set up at places like Picacho and Rice in California, Parker across the border in Arizona and at Searchlight, Nevada. Sometimes, when crews were working near a town, board was a hotel and the men ate like kings with their $1.95 daily food allowance. "That was 65 cents a meal and you couldn't eat all the food 65 cents would buy in those days," said Al Preston, whose surveying days started in 1925 when he began ferrying crews up and down the river in boats he had built.

Life for the surveyors offered little more than fresh air and a regular job as the United States drifted toward and then plunged into the Great Depression.

Model-A wagons added welcome horsepower to desert travel.

IT WAS GRUELING, PAINSTAKINGLY SLOW WORK ACROSS A LANDSCAPE ALMOST ENTIRELY DEVOID OF ROADS.

"There wasn't much to do in the desert until construction days, but I do remember one night in 1927 when we were camped at Rice," recalled Preston. "We heard that Mrs. Brown, who ran the post office, had a broken radio. One of our guys fixed it so we could all hear the second Dempsey-Tunney fight. Even then, we couldn't hear too much and just as

Permanent surveyors camp (above) was home on the desert; fly camp (right) was more like a hotel for the night.

the announcer yelled, 'He's down,' the radio signal faded out completely. It took us a week to find out that Tunney had whipped Dempsey again."

The surveyors' daily regimen was a repetitious tramping over the desert and mountains, only infrequently broken up by a fierce sandstorm or freak winter snowstorm. Day after day, they carefully took the measure of the land. Progress was steady but slow; two or three miles was a good day's work considering the harsh terrain and hostile climate. Men worked in parties of four or five. Each was led by a party chief who was assisted by an instrumentman, a chainman and one or two rodmen. In the final years they would be joined by engineers and geologists. Everyone had to carry his own 30-pound pack, as well as a share of the surveying equipment which included a cumbersome wooden transit that was used to make measurements, and what seemed to be an inexhaustible supply of wooden stakes. Hansel- and Gretel-like, those stakes trailed behind them, wooden "crumbs" that marked their lonely but purposeful journey. Years later those stakes and the men who hammered them into the earth were still remembered.

"If all of the stakes we banged into the desert had sprouted, we'd have quite a forest today," said surveyor Joe Chiriaco. "My god, we had talent on that job," added Witt. "In the last few years, when the Depression started to be felt, all of the surveyors were experienced enough to be party chiefs. We had guys with master's degrees pounding in those stakes."

During the survey era all sorts of schemes were explored, no matter how fanciful they might seem. There was a proposal at one point to have an aqueduct that didn't rely on a storage dam. There also was the ongoing argument as to whether the aqueduct should operate by gravity or with pumps. The idea of an aqueduct without a reservoir surfaced in late 1926 when surveying focused on a spot north of Blythe, California. The area appeared to be the ideal diversion point for the most direct, practical aqueduct route. There was only one flaw with the plan; there wasn't a suitable site for a dam in the area. Boulder Dam still hadn't been approved by Congress and any aqueduct from the Colorado needed some mechanism for desilting the river's water. Before the Colorado was dammed, it carried a tremendous burden of earth. Al Preston remembered, "It's hard to realize how muddy it was. We used to stir four spoons of canned milk into a bucket of water to coagulate the mud at the bottom so we could drink the water. It was useless the way it was in the river."

In the gravity-flow-versus-pump-lift debate, proponents of an all-gravity system contended that type of aqueduct would not only be cheaper to build but also would be less costly to operate. They could point to the performance of the all-gravity Los Angeles Aqueduct, which had been in operation for more than a decade. Pump-lift advocates countered with the argument that there were only a limited number of possible routes for a gravity-flow aqueduct because the system had to begin and end at fixed elevations. They believed an aqueduct with pumps could be directed along any number of potential routes to ensure a more economical project.

Ultimately, Frank Weymouth, Metropolitan's first chief engineer, and his staff would make the decision on the recommendation for the aqueduct's type and route. Their decision would require validation by an engineering board of review and the endorsement of Metropolitan's board of directors, which had the final say. Weymouth and his assistants opted for the Parker route in late November 1930, after an exhaustive review of seven years of surveying data.

Gear stowed and ready to move on — dog and all

The route called for the aqueduct to originate above a dam site north of Parker, Arizona. From there it headed west via Rice, climbed over Shaver's Summit (today known as Chiriaco Summit, named for the surveyor), passed through the flank of the Little San Bernardino Mountains north of the Coachella Valley and burrowed through the heart of Mt. San Jacinto into Riverside County. The aqueduct would terminate at either of two reservoir sites, Cajalco in Riverside County or Puddingstone in Los Angeles County. Weymouth's recommendation also called on the federal government to construct Parker Dam on the Colorado to provide a storage reservoir for the aqueduct. Weymouth was convinced that the Parker route was clearly the best choice. It was the most economical and geologically safest of the more than 100 surveyed. Additionally, the Parker route lay completely inside California so that it would not be subject to taxation by another state.

Three of the most distinguished American engineers of the day, operating as the required board of review, examined Weymouth's conclusions. Thaddeus Merriman, chief engineer of the New York City Water Supply System and designer of that city's Catskill Aqueduct; A.J. Wiley, consulting engineer, who had worked on the Panama Canal and who would later work on the Boulder (Hoover) Dam project; and Richard Lyman, chairman of the University of Utah's school of civil engineering, confirmed Weymouth's choice, choosing the Parker Route over seven alternatives, thus closing the long debate over a gravity-flow system.

The board had discarded the two gravity-flow routes included in the seven alternatives which involved ambitious engineering feats by 1930 or even 1991 standards. In the case of the Bridge Canyon Project, Merriman, Wiley and Lyman concluded that at an estimated price of $500 million, "it is more expensive than any of the pumping routes, traverses the most difficult geological terrain and presents no offsetting benefit of any kind." The trio found the second, the San Juan Project, which was even more grandiose and carried a budget as large as its scope, $1 billion, to be "entirely beyond the possibility of realization."

The review board had then moved on to consider the five other alternatives. Four — the Black Canyon, Bulls Head, Picacho and all-American routes — called for huge pumping plants to lift water over the mountains and involved either siting the aqueduct along a major, active earthquake fault — the San Andreas — or more expense than the Parker route. The last alternative, the southern sea level route, had an international aspect. Specifications, which also required pumps, called for diverting water out

Desert life was hot, dry and remote.

THE BOARD GAVE WEYMOUTH THE GO-AHEAD ON FINAL PLANS FOR THE AQUEDUCT.

Some survey parties needed horses to cross rugged terrain.

of the Colorado south of Yuma, Arizona, into a desilting basin in Mexico, through an aqueduct and tunnel west to San Diego where it would then be pumped up the Southern California coast.

Five weeks after the review board issued its report, Metropolitan's board of directors gathered on January 16, 1931, and unanimously went on record for the Parker route. The board also gave Weymouth the go-ahead on final plans for the aqueduct, which would entail more extensive surveys of the chosen route. The stage was set for going to the voters with a $220 million bond issue to pay for the Colorado River Aqueduct.

While the surveyors once again headed back for the now familiar desert, Metropolitan geared up for the election which was scheduled for that September. The campaign was a masterful performance, orchestrated by Don Kinsey, a public relations wizard who served as an assistant to Weymouth.

The old Rice Road

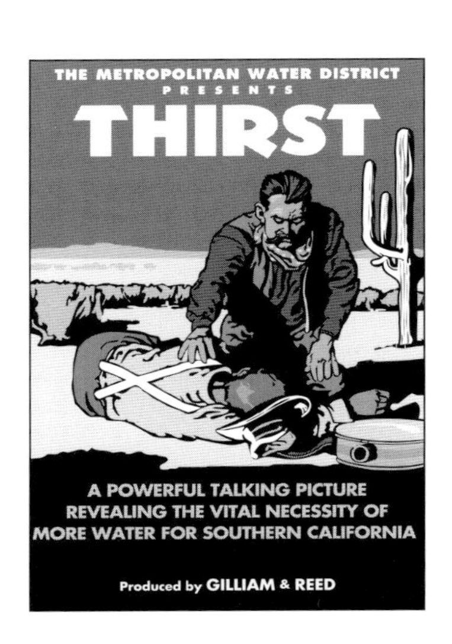

Andrew Gram, then the executive secretary of Metropolitan's board of directors, recalled Kinsey's contribution. "He got the jump on the opposition from the very start and kept them on the defensive throughout the election. Remember this was the early part of the Depression and imagine selling people on the idea of voting for $220 million in bonds. But Kinsey built a very strong case on the need for employment and the huge number of jobs the aqueduct would provide."

Thousands of people walked the precincts for the bonds. One was Les Martin, who would start working for Metropolitan the next year. "No one I talked to in Orange County ever thought they'd live to see the need for the water," Martin said, "but most of them said they'd vote for anything that would provide 10,000 jobs."

The 1931 Depression-era family made use of free beaches for recreation, but voted yes to pay for water for their children's future.

Kinsey knew how to seize every opportunity to promote the aqueduct and creatively used all of the communications outlets of the day. Story after story rolled out of typewriters and a series of dramatic radio programs hit the airwaves. Kinsey helped produce one of the first talking motion pictures, a short epic titled "Thirst," that was shown in 200 movie theaters. He had organized labor, religious leaders, civic and service groups, women's clubs and movie studio chiefs to endorse the aqueduct, and recruited Senator Hiram Johnson and Congressman Phil Swing, the leaders of the Boulder Dam fight, to address large rallies. On election morning, every bottle of milk delivered in Southern California arrived with printed reminders to cast a vote for the bonds.

This strategy stopped the opposition cold, and the bond issue won in a landslide, by a margin approaching 5-1 (224,477 yes, 46,338 no).

The way was clear for construction of the Colorado River Aqueduct. However, legal requirements and the worsening U.S. economy presented temporary delays. According to the MWD Act, the bond election and Metropolitan's authority to collect a property tax to pay for bonds had to

be validated. This barrier was cleared by a favorable ruling of the state Supreme Court in June 1932. But by this time, the bottom had dropped out of the market for municipal bonds as the Depression deepened. For nearly a year, Metropolitan officials worked with Congress and other federal officers to set up the complicated authority for the Reconstruction Finance Corporation to purchase MWD bonds. Finally, on December 12, 1932, the first block of slightly more than $2 million in bonds was sold to the RFC; six weeks later it was full steam ahead on the gargantuan job of building the Colorado River Aqueduct.

Aqueduct construction workers

Chapter 6

ACROSS THE SANDS AND THROUGH THE MOUNTAINS

Frank Weymouth had iron-like determination that was mirrored in the color of his steel gray hair. As Metropolitan's first general manager and chief engineer, he assumed all responsibility for construction of the Colorado River Aqueduct, a project that would prove the capstone of a distinguished career. Working for the Bureau of Reclamation, he had built some of the world's largest dams and his expert testimony had played a vital role in winning Congressional approval for Boulder Dam. Weymouth's strength of purpose would serve him well as he tackled this vast and complicated project of tremendous responsibility. His mind and energy were fixed on two goals: completing the Colorado River Aqueduct on schedule and within budget.

WEYMOUTH'S MIND AND ENERGY WERE FIXED ON TWO GOALS: COMPLETING THE COLORADO RIVER AQUEDUCT ON SCHEDULE AND WITHIN BUDGET.

People working for Weymouth knew he was determined to achieve those goals. "Weymouth was so highly motivated by the aqueduct project that it was the single purpose in his life," observed Robert Skinner, who worked as an aqueduct engineer, later becoming one of Weymouth's successors. "When he said something had to be done by a certain time, it had to be done and no excuses. His goal was to have the project finished and water served in 1941 and nothing would ever permit him to deviate his attention from that."

Facing Weymouth and his army of aqueduct builders was a monumental, some would say awesome, task. The Parker route stretched 242 miles from the Colorado into Southern California. Twenty-nine separate tunnels stretching 92 miles would have to be blasted and bored. Four dams had to be built. Five plants with powerful pumps capable of lifting water more than 1,600 feet along the route were required. These facilities would bring water to the edge of Metropolitan's service area at the aqueduct's terminal reservoir (now called Lake Mathews) in Riverside County. Another complex system of works — 156 miles of distribution lines, eight additional tunnels and a softening and treatment plant — was needed to serve water to Metropolitan's 13 member cities.

Without argument, Weymouth was the driving force behind launching legions of workmen into the desert and spurring them on to complete this enormous enterprise according to his fixed timetable. But this was far from being a one-man show. Supporting Weymouth was an unusually talented and brilliant team. It included among others, Julian Hinds, the assistant chief engineer; W. B. Mathews, the general counsel; and Robert Diemer, the distribution engineer. These and other Weymouth lieutenants left their personal stamp on the aqueduct. Hinds' forte was in design and his genius is reflected in many elements of the aqueduct. Curiously, he joined Metropolitan in 1930 somewhat reluctantly. He had been asked to design Boulder Dam, at the same time Metropolitan sought his services. Years later, Hinds would reflect on the unique choice he had been forced to make, wistfully wishing that he had been "born twins" so he might have worked on both projects.

Mathews was at home in the rough and tumble arena of politics. He had been instrumental in the long fight to win Congressional passage of the Boulder Dam Project Act. It was Mathews who had negotiated the contracts that gave Metropolitan its 1 million-plus acre-foot share of water from the Colorado and, equally important, 36 percent of the power produced at Boulder Dam. This energy would run the pumps that lifted the water over the mountains. However, Mathews' reputation as a deal-maker did have its downside.

"Mathews loved to argue and negotiate. But he was a victim of his friends and politicians who would walk into his office all the time," recalled Andrew Gram, the executive secretary of MWD's board of directors. "It got so bad that we had to get him two offices: one for his friends and a second, hidden one, where he would get his work done."

On the other hand, Diemer was the perfect extension of Weymouth. Gruff and blustery, he was the hard-driving field engineer who got things done, winning the grudging respect of those working for him. "I never

Payday along the aqueduct project

fought with a boss more than I did with Diemer, and I never liked a boss more than Diemer," said Jack Zapp, who was a resident engineer on three tunnel projects. "With Diemer, you would argue out something to the finish and the subject would never come up again. He just wanted to know what was on your mind."

Weymouth picked his team well. In the nine years it would take to build the aqueduct, they would encounter all sorts of unexpected challenges including labor unrest, a farcical "war" with Arizona and a reservoir that seemingly vanished, but they surmounted each test. A quartet of his associates — Hinds, Diemer, Skinner and Hank Mills — would succeed Weymouth as Metropolitan's next four general managers.

Assembling the vast army of workmen who would build the aqueduct was perhaps the least of the many challenges facing Metropolitan. Certainly, there was no shortage of skilled and unskilled labor. The numbing reality of the Depression was sinking in across the country, and there were thousands of men eager to do the backbreaking, hot, dirty work of pouring concrete, shoveling rubble out of newly blasted tunnels, or hammering rivets. Records show that more than 100,000 men applied for work on the aqueduct at Metropolitan's employment offices. In addition, thousands more sought employment from contractors hired by Metropolitan

"I GOT $5.50 A DAY FOR MYSELF AND ANOTHER $5.50 A SHIFT FOR THE USE OF MY TRUCK."

Chiseling a canal out of rock

for specific jobs. Ultimately, it took the sweat and strain, ingenuity and invention of more than 35,000 men to conquer the desert.

"Those days were really something; guys were selling apples on the street to make money," said Bill Merrithew, who became a chainman in February 1933. "A job that paid $100 a month was so important to so many people that you would do anything to get it. It was about the only damned job in the state."

"The district played an awful big part in the survival of the working man," added survey veteran Al Preston. "You worked hard and had no one special job. You learned to do a little bit of everything."

(Top) Repair shop on the desert and (bottom) surveyor-turned-aqueduct-worker Al Preston

The experiences of workers Bud Fields and Benny Lamm were typical. They had no promise or guarantee of a permanent job and, like many of the men whose sweat built the aqueduct, drifted across the desert from project to project. Fields, for example, was driving a truck for a freight company that was going bankrupt in 1933.

"My salary had just been cut to 38 cents an hour, so I applied for work with MWD. I was offered a job as a truck skinner (driver) if I could bring my own truck. I borrowed some money for a down payment and bought one on time to get the job. I got $5.50 a day for myself and another $5.50 a shift for the use of my truck," said Fields. "I was on day wages the whole time. It was a day-to-day thing for most of the guys working there. When one project ran out, you had to look for another."

Lamm, meanwhile, found his first position with Metropolitan in 1934 as a mechanic in the Los Angeles garage. He was hired for one month. Lamm moved on to the desert where he built a workshop at Little Morongo Canyon and spent the next five years shifting from project to project to stay employed. "I must have had more job classifications than just about anyone — mechanic, chuck tender, laborer, compressorman, blacksmith," he said. “Finally, when they opened the pumping plant at Iron Mountain in 1939, they offered me what we were all looking for, a permanent job.”

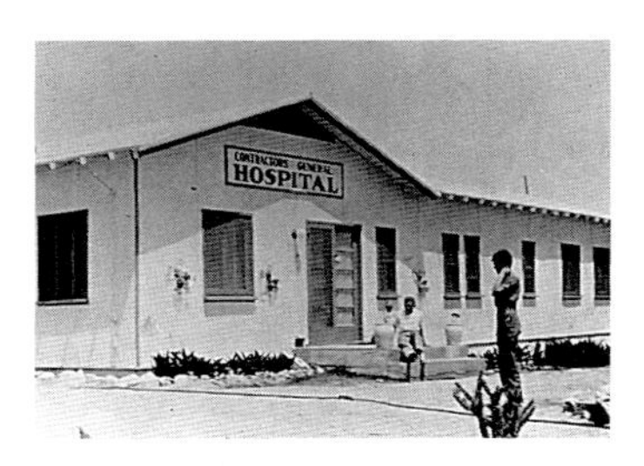

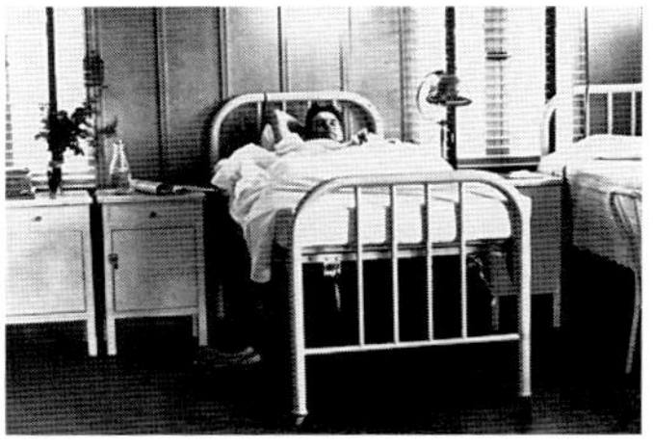

The first health maintenance organization (HMO)

Besides having some usable skills, Lamm, Fields and the thousands of others like them had to be residents of one of Metropolitan’s member cities for at least one year to qualify for employment. But that didn’t prevent men from other parts of the state, as well as the rest of the country, from descending on Southern California in their hungry quest for work. Once here, they weren’t above a bit of flimflammery to prove they were qualified.

“Many fellows who weren’t district residents went directly to contractors for work but would usually only get a couple days in before we caught up with them,” said Hank Mills, who verified workers’ eligibility as part of his job as a resident engineer. “I had to check them before they went to work, but it was an impossible task. I’d check a camp after dinner and men would pass around their voter registration slips, which proved their residency, to all their friends.”

Lots of men simply purchased phony proof of residence. The most notorious address for hire was 521 San Julian Street, according to aqueduct veteran Les Martin. “I never came across so many people who lived in the same place. Men would pay $5 to the owner just to use the address. It was a flophouse in downtown Los Angeles with 20 rooms and 2,000 registrants. But where else could the district find hardrock miners? They never lived anywhere for any period of time and just drifted around all over the country from job to job. You’d call up 521 San Julian and ask if a certain man lived there. And if he’d paid his $5, the owner would say yes.”

It took all kinds of men to build the aqueduct. A small minority were happy with a few days labor, just enough to sustain them before moving on to something else. The majority craved the chance to work, even under the desiccating desert heat. Unemployed professionals worked alongside unschooled laborers, mucking out tunnels. Hardrock miners, down from Montana, dodged the residency requirements to find employment as did doctors, lawyers and at least one ex-society playboy. Store clerks who lost their jobs and wound up on tunneling crews were tagged with the nickname of "1936 miners."

A few of the thousands who labored left an indelible stamp on the job through their deeds or personalities. These were men like "Doughbelly" LaPlante, Sidney Garfield and Ralph "Pistol Pete" Stringfellow. La Plante was a tough miner who gained aqueduct immortality at one Fourth of July celebration in Indio by wrestling a bear borrowed from a traveling carnival.

Ambulance and crew

The contributions of Garfield and Stringfellow were of an entirely different nature. The two arrived in the desert in the spring of 1933, shortly after the start of construction.

Garfield, a young doctor, was a recent graduate of the University of Southern California's medical school. He conceived a unique idea — an idea that later would have far-reaching consequences in American medicine. He would provide onsite workers' health care.

After turning down Metropolitan's low-paying offer to work at a small hospital it had built in Indio, Garfield, with borrowed money, established his own hospital in the tiny community of Desert Center. The 12-bed facility boasted one of the area's first air conditioning units when it opened in October 1933. By the middle of the following year, Garfield was going broke trying to collect fees from men making just $4 or $5 a day. Insurance companies, which provided contractors with medical coverage for industrial accidents, didn't refer many patients and compensated him poorly for those he did treat. But one company, Industrial Indemnity Exchange, saved the day by suggesting a prepayment plan. The company agreed to pay Garfield 10 percent of its premium if the doctor would assume responsibility for all on-the-job medical care covered by the firm. The idea was so successful that Garfield later suggested expanding medical coverage for complete health care for the aqueduct workers.

Winston Brothers tent camp at site of Parker Dam

"It was obvious to me, the contractors and the insurance companies that it was better for all of us if the workers stayed healthy and didn't get hurt on the job," said Garfield, who was to promote a type of preventive medicine that would become both widely practiced and well-accepted. This early prepayment plan employed by Garfield in the desert was popular and inexpensive. For a nickel a day, an amount deducted from their paychecks, workers received unlimited medical care from Garfield. The price was right and about 90 percent of the men enrolled in the program. Garfield later built a second hospital near Parker Dam, as well as opening first-aid stations at all other major construction sites. Still later, he set up a prepaid health care program at Grand Coulee Dam in the state of Washington and at several West Coast shipyards during World War II. Following the war he founded the Kaiser Permanente health care system with the backing of industrialist Henry J. Kaiser.

Pistol Pete Stringfellow was a former Texas Ranger and deputy U.S. marshal, the epitome of the old-time western lawman. Lean and steely-eyed, this "tough cop" brought law and order along the aqueduct route, patrolling its entire length armed with a pocketful of badges identifying him as a Metropolitan special agent and a deputy sheriff for San Bernardino, Riverside and Los Angeles counties. He and the .38 automatic he packed were the law and Stringfellow earned the respect of the work crews. He was tough and fearless. He had to be to dive in between hardrock miners to break up a barroom brawl.

But Stringfellow also had a softer side and was remembered by aqueduct veterans not only as a hardboiled cop with a quick sense of humor but as a friend who would deliver paychecks to workers in remote desert locations.

"Pistol Pete" Stringfellow

Pistol Pete Stringfellow was the epitome of the old-time western lawman.

Shortly after Christmas in 1932, the nine-year job of building the aqueduct got under way with little fanfare. Workmen arrived in the desert to launch necessary support operations. First priorities included building water, power and telephone systems, as well as hundreds of miles of highways and roads. The vast desert wilderness of southeastern California had to be readied for the thousands of workmen expected in 1933. Camps, where the workers would be fed and housed, had to be constructed.

Each of these projects was a major building operation. For example,

Placing forms on the Eagle Mountain siphon

providing for the water was almost like putting together a miniature municipal system: quite a feat with water sources scarce — only a few scattered springs and wells. Still, enough water for a city of 15,000 had to be developed. It was estimated that much water would be needed each day to cool the men and machines working in the furnace-like temperatures of the desert and to mix the tons of concrete that would be necessary. The search for water began with drilling operations that eventually resulted in 14 productive wells. Water from these wells was distributed through a system of 199 miles of pipelines and 35 reservoirs and tanks.

Weymouth divided the thousands of aqueduct laborers into two divisions. One, composed of workmen employed directly by Metropolitan, was categorized as "force-account work." The other, operated by a variety of the largest construction contractors in the West, competitively bid and were awarded individual contracts for projects such as powerlines, tunnels, siphons or sections of canal.

On January 25, 1933, actual work on the aqueduct began at two separate locations in the Little San Bernardino Mountains. From that day until June 1941, when the aqueduct and distribution system were finally completed, work rarely stopped. Men labored around the clock in three eight-hour shifts and normally worked 12 consecutive days before receiving two days off. Some worked even longer stretches to complete vital projects. Sam Thomason, who worked with crews building power transmission lines that would connect Boulder Dam and the aqueduct, remembered once working an ll-hour shift for 72 straight days.

Such grueling schedules were maintained in the desert throughout the construction years despite the climate. Bill Merrithew, who maintained a weather station at one camp, never forgot the monotonous, numbing, near-killing heat. "I wasn't allowed to tell the men how hot it got out there. But the station was in the shade and I saw the thermometer hit

126 degrees a number of times. It seemed like it was always over 120. I lost 40 pounds in that desert over three summers," he said.

The annual summer shutdown of above-ground concrete work from mid-June through mid-September was the only concession made for the heat. Engineers suspended surface concrete work because they feared the blistering heat would prevent the material from curing properly, thus losing strength. The only other delays during the nine years of construction resulted from political and labor disputes.

Hot rivets on the fly

Legal and political posturing by Arizona halted work on Parker Dam during parts of 1934 and 1935. Two years later, a strike stopped work on the San Jacinto Tunnel. However, a tribute rather than a dispute brought a brief systemwide work stoppage in 1935 when Bill Mulholland, responsible for selecting the Colorado River a dozen years earlier, died. Several days later, Weymouth ordered work to stop up and down the aqueduct for a two-minute silence during his funeral.

Robert Phillips, then a young worker in the Copper Basin Tunnel who years later was to head the Los Angeles Department of Water and Power, had vivid memories of those quiet moments. "Tunnels were usually very noisy places with all kinds of machinery operating, and even the smallest sounds were magnified and reverberated. But that day everything was dead silent and everything stopped. I leaned on my shovel for the two minutes. It surprised the hell out of me that these men so far from the funeral would honor Mulholland."

Then the relentless work resumed to meet Weymouth's inexorable schedule. Driving the 29 tunnels became the heart of the matter because such construction was terribly tedious and time consuming. With the first boring in early 1933, a number of critical decisions, crucial to the aqueduct's construction, already had been made. Facilities such as the tunnels, sections of open canal and covered conduits would be built to the aqueduct's

THERE WOULD BE FLOODS AND A MAJOR STRIKE BEFORE THE TUNNEL WAS FINALLY DRIVEN.

ultimate full capacity of more than 1 billion gallons of water a day. Other features, including 144 siphons, would be constructed to half capacity while each of the pumping plants along the aqueduct would initially hold only three pumps, one-third of design capacity. In later years, when demand for the river's water increased, these facilities could be expanded. But the tunnels, lined with concrete, could never be widened and, consequently, had initially to be blasted to their permanent diameter.

Driving 97 miles of tunnels meant chiseling a passage as wide as 20 feet through the unyielding heart of a mountain. The work was dirty, dangerous and deliberate. Hardrock miners ripped through one of the shorter tunnels — Wide Canyon Number 2 — in months, finishing it on October 2, 1933. But it took another five years before the final one was holed out. Progress was measured in feet. Tunnel crews averaged an advance of six feet on each heading per eight-hour shift throughout this phase of construction. Considered excellent, this speed was made possible as the result of new tunneling techniques and equipment developed several years earlier for the construction of Boulder Dam and modified for use along the aqueduct.

One piece of equipment — the jumbo — was a mammoth framework that could accommodate up to 11 compressed air drills, allowing a crew of miners to cut into the entire face of the heading they were driving. It was so large, an electric locomotive was needed to pull and push it into position. As many as 72 holes, incisions as deep as 12 feet and an inch and a quarter in diameter, would be drilled into a heading from a jumbo. Each hole was packed with blasting powder and fired by an electric detonator equipped with delays to trigger a special firing sequence. Each blast pattern was prepared to consider the hardness and tightness of the rock. The result was a carefully timed series of explosions, the first ripping open the center of the heading and subsequent blasts cutting the sides, top and bottom of the tunnel. Compressors then cleared the air in the tunnel, sucking up the dusty, pulverized rock, and finally — usually within half an hour — crews reentered the tunnel to begin clearing out the rubble.

Though work in the tunnels was dirty and the danger of cave-ins an ever-present hazard, at least it was cooler than sweating outside under the blazing desert sun. "I was lucky I worked the day shift, so I missed the outside heat," remembered Phillips. "It was cool in the tunnels, but when you left the portal to go back to camp it was like walking into an oven. The only time it got hot inside was when we were pouring concrete to line the tunnels. Drying concrete gives off plenty of heat."

The Potrero bunch

The men who split open the mountains were a hard-working and hard-drinking lot. Much of their off-hours imbibing was done in an Indio bar aptly named the Jackhammer. It was a legendary watering hole that more than one miner swore was vital to the building of the aqueduct. "The place was like Disneyland," said engineer Jack Zapp. "People would come down from Los Angeles just to see the show those drunken miners put on. Once, when someone from Hollywood complained about the lack of fighting, one miner calmly asked the spectator who he should hit."

A more formidable foe was Mt. San Jacinto. At 10,831 feet, the second tallest mountain in Southern California, it stood squarely in the path of the aqueduct. A 13-mile-long tunnel had to lance the mountain, a task that would take five and one half years. There would be floods and a major strike before the tunnel was finally driven. On May 12, 1933, the metamorphic monster was attacked from several different directions. Two vertical shafts were excavated to the grade level of the tunnel at Cabazon on the east and at Potrero on the west, giving the crews working for Metropolitan's contractor four headings to work from in addition to those at the eastern and western portals.

But Mt. San Jacinto had a few surprises in store. The mountain's interior was laced with subsurface faults, streams and springs. In July 1934, miners

(Top) Tunnels were noisy, but cool and (bottom) lunch underground

operating in the Potrero shaft hit an underground stream; water roaring into the tunnel had to be pumped out and a second flood disabled two of the three pumps. Then in November an even bigger deluge inundated the tunnel. More than 15,000 gallons of water a minute spilled down on the miners, forcing another evacuation.

"The water came in with a big, mad rush and filled the shaft to the top. Miners scrambled up the 800-foot ladder to the surface, and the last man out made it with water swirling around his waist. We knew there was water in that mountain, but not that much," recalled Zapp, who witnessed the near-tragedy.

Again the shaft was pumped out, but progress on the tunnel was excruciatingly slow. After 18 months, less than two of the 13 miles had been excavated. So in January 1935, Weymouth fired the contractor and decided to have Metropolitan's own engineers and men complete the job. Larger pumps were pressed into service to control flooding and suck up the water that constantly dripped from the walls. In early 1936, the Potrero West and West Portal headings joined up. Seven months later, the East Portal was breached. The two ends of the tunnel were complete, but a six-mile stretch straight through the heart of Mt. San Jacinto still remained unpierced.

Tunnel inspection

Once more the mountain had to be attacked — but this time from a new angle. By digging a mile-long lateral shaft called the Lawrence Adit, two more headings were opened. Mt. San Jacinto was almost conquered. Yet the battle still dragged on, but this time it was a labor dispute in August 1937 that held up operations. The International Union of Mine, Mill and Smelter Workers had organized locals at several aqueduct work sites including Mt. San Jacinto. When Metropolitan's board of directors refused to accept 16 demands submitted by the local, the union called a strike. On August 14, all but 206 of a total working crew of about 1,190 men walked off the job; violence briefly flared up and tunneling progress all but stopped. Metropolitan management held fast and, within six weeks, tunnel work was back to normal, with the men ready for the final push. It would take 13 anticlimactic months to finish up the job; Mt. San Jacinto had been defeated with the completion of the Lawrence Adit. On November 19, 1939, a charge of celebratory powder shattered the last thin wall of rock. The giant mountain had been conquered; the tunnel had been holed through.

At the opposite end of the aqueduct, along the Colorado River, another

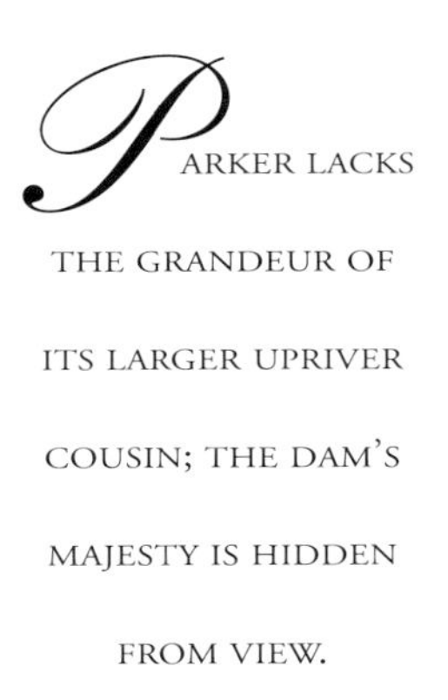
PARKER LACKS THE GRANDEUR OF ITS LARGER UPRIVER COUSIN; THE DAM'S MAJESTY IS HIDDEN FROM VIEW.

Parker Dam construction site at night

drama had unfolded. In February 1934, the federal Bureau of Reclamation began work on Parker Dam despite the protests of Arizona, which still was against any river development. A month later when cables were strung across the river to the Arizona side to help anchor a barge, Governor B.B. Moeur called up the National Guard. Moeur was determined to prevent the dam from being built. The Arizona shore where the cable had been anchored was remote, so the owners of the Julia B, a ferry boat at Parker, Arizona, volunteered to carry the first two soldiers up the river. A worn, aging 45-foot vessel powered by a Model T engine, the Julia B had been built more than a decade earlier by Al Preston, one of the men now working on the California side of the river to build the aqueduct. But the ferry, nicknamed "The Arizona Navy" by Los Angeles Times reporter Chester Hanson, just couldn't do the job. She was too tall to clear the low-hanging cables strung across the river. Eventually the two Arizona soldiers were hauled by motorboat up the river to a campsite where they were ordered to spy on the dam builders. Three days later they were reinforced by half a dozen Arizona national guardsmen who arrived by car after a bone-shaking ride over an old wagon road.

For eight months the Arizonans merely observed the continuing work on the dam. However, as a trestle bridge crept ever closer to the Arizona bank, Governor Moeur became increasingly bellicose. On November 10, he declared martial law, ordering the National Guard to prevent further construction and protect the state's sovereignty. Upwards of 100 men, some armed with machine guns, were ordered to the front. Fortunately, cooler heads prevailed. The Secretary of the Interior halted work on the dam as the battlefield shifted to the U.S. Supreme Court, where the combatants traded briefs instead of bullets. Arizona won the first skirmish. The federal government instituted a suit against Arizona to prevent any interference with Parker Dam. The court held for Arizona in April 1935 because the project had never received Congressional approval. Four months later, Congress rectified that oversight and this curious chapter in aqueduct history drew to a close.

The "Arizona Navy"

Looking at Parker Dam today, one can easily fail to appreciate the passions its construction generated or understand why it was considered to be an engineering marvel once it was built. Indeed, Parker lacks the grandeur of its larger upriver cousin, Boulder (Hoover) Dam, since it only rises 85 feet above the river's surface. Actually, the dam's majesty is hidden from view for it reaches 235 feet beneath the Colorado to the bedrock upon which the structure is anchored.

Parker Dam, funded with Metropolitan money, was swiftly completed in only three years, once the Arizona "war" was settled. A key element in the Colorado River Aqueduct system, the dam formed Lake Havasu, creating the source reservoir for the aqueduct. Turbines in the dam generate power, half of which was allocated to Metropolitan to pump Lake Havasu water to Southern California.

The aqueduct system required substantially more power than was available from Parker Dam; the balance, therefore, was created 150 miles upstream at Boulder Dam. A 237-mile network of high voltage transmission lines and towers was strung across the desert and mountains to link the two dams to the aqueduct. The highline crews who built and later maintained the power system were as free-wheeling a bunch as any in the desert. But the hot lines they worked on required steady men and sound judgment. "You had to be reliable to work with 230,000 volts," recalled crew member Sam Thomason. "You couldn't work with cobwebs in your head."

Concrete curing

Elsewhere there were unique challenges requiring innovative solutions. The first batch of concrete, the prime ingredient of the aqueduct, was poured in January 1934 at the Fan Hill siphon. That job, like all others on the aqueduct, was conducted under the ever-present eyes of graduates of "Tuthill Tech," a school for concrete inspectors. Testing engineer Lewis Tuthill, who ran a one-week course for more than 200 inspectors at Metropolitan's field headquarters in Banning, also operated a laboratory where he focused on finding the best way to cure concrete in the desert.

"Heat wasn't the big problem, we just didn't have all that much water available," he said. "Curing is simply doing whatever needs to be done to keep concrete from totally drying out. If it dries out too fast it loses strength. If it continues to hold water, even for weeks, it will continue to strengthen. In those days, we kept concrete wet after it was poured by covering it with wet burlap or carpeting. But we knew we wouldn't be able to get enough of those materials in the desert, let alone the water required."

So Tuthill experimented. New asphalt-based sealing compounds were tried, but these blackish substances drew heat into concrete. When coal tars were developed, Tuthill smeared them on concrete and they proved to be a partial solution. Eventually, Tuthill sprayed whitewash over coal tar and he solved the curing problem.

Clyde Wood, one of the contractors employed by Metropolitan, made a unique contribution to the construction effort by devising machines to cut and pave the 62 miles of open canals. Wood's ungainly creations appeared to have been inspired by the H.G. Wells story "War of the Worlds," but they did the job faster than conventional methods. He used his canal trimmer to cut the 55-foot-wide canal to its exact shape. The giant machine, which rode on tracks set on both banks of the canal, was put to work after a rough course had been scooped out of the desert. The trimmer lumbered down the tracks, ejecting a stream of rock, dirt and sand onto the desert floor. After the canal was reinforced with rods, Wood's equally-awkward paving machine operated as a giant trowel, laying and tamping down a coat of concrete along the bottom and flanks at the rate of more than a foot a minute. Narrow-gauge rail cars supplied the paver with fresh concrete. Wood's machines worked so well that he even leased them to other contractors working for Metropolitan.

Original plans for the aqueduct called for four pumping plants, but a fifth had to be added at Iron Mountain. It became necessary to shift the route of a section of the aqueduct when miners couldn't bore through the Granite Mountains because the soft, constantly crumbling rock made tunneling impossible. This change meant 15 huge pumps, rather than the originally planned 12, would be needed to boost the water on its way to Southern California.

Canal taking shape

CBS documents the completion of the aqueduct.

As enormous amounts of energy would be consumed, it became essential to design the most efficient pumps. A pump-testing laboratory was installed at the California Institute of Technology in Pasadena where Metropolitan engineers and Cal Tech researchers worked two years to devise specifications for the pumps, which were installed in the five desert pumping plants by early 1939. By spring the work crews were talking about an upcoming wet run. The eastern half of the aqueduct would be tested, all 121 miles from Copper Basin Reservoir, near Metropolitan's Colorado River field headquarters at Gene, to Hayfield (later renamed Hinds after Julian Hinds), the final pumping plant.

Larry Green, who would become Metropolitan's supervisor of maintenance in the desert, was there that day in May when the aqueduct was turned on for the first time. "It was quite a thrill to watch the water flow through the canals and I followed it all the way into Hayfield in my pickup. Some of the guys were claiming it would never work because they thought the aqueduct went uphill in some places."

The doubters were wrong. The aqueduct functioned exactly as designed, from beginning to end. Adjacent to the Hayfield Pumping Plant was what appeared to be a natural reservoir site, and it began to fill up with Colorado River water. But like a mirage, the little lake vanished when the pumping was reduced. Because subsurface soil at Hayfield turned out to be too porous to retain water, the reservoir, never a critical element of the system, was abandoned.

Five months later, on October 14, 1939, work on the aqueduct portion of the project was completed with a flourish. Festivities included speeches, music and a nationwide radio broadcast as the final concrete was poured at the West Portal of the San Jacinto Tunnel. There was, however, still much work to be done farther west. The complex distribution system — with its treatment and softening plant, tunnels and 156 miles of feeder

Sculpting the district seal

lines — was under construction, and work begun in 1936 would stretch on for another 20 months well into 1941. Still, the Colorado River Aqueduct was completed on time; the 35,000 men who had labored tirelessly had beaten Frank Weymouth's tough deadline.

Chapter 7

WAR AND PEACE, ANNEXATION AND EXPANSION

It was going to be an era of surprises and opportunity. Southern California and the entire state would change forever in the 1940s and '50s. California was about to step onto the national and even world stages. No longer would it be dismissed as some vague place "out on the West Coast." More than ever before, California would become a desirable place to live and work. Hundreds of thousands of servicemen would pass through the Southland during World War II and the memories of the mild, sunny climate would entice many of them to return in the post-war boom days. Not only was the state about to become a center of finance, industry and culture, but it was on its way to becoming the nation's most populous.

THE VAST, BLAZING DESERT HAD EVERYTHING PATTON REQUIRED FOR HIS ARMY EXCEPT WATER.

The phenomenal changes would tax California's available resources, particularly its water supply. Yet, curiously, Metropolitan began the post-aqueduct construction days with an unexpected surplus. In 1941, water became so plentiful that Metropolitan could hardly give it away, much less sell it. A shift in climate, starting in 1937, had abruptly altered Southern California's cyclical weather pattern from dry to very wet and depleted groundwater basins recovered from years of overpumping. Therefore, when the Colorado River Aqueduct went into service in June of 1941, communities felt no real need to purchase the water. So Metropolitan's board of directors decided to give it away and offered to deliver free water to its member agencies for 60 days. Ten of the 13 accepted the offer and took slightly more than 7,000 acre-feet. That was almost as much as Metropolitan would sell in the following 10 months.

Although the district had a temporary marketing problem, America's entrance into World War II would create a renewed demand for water. Southern California industry tooled up for the war and became a vital contributor of material to the "arsenal of democracy" called for by President Franklin D. Roosevelt. The number and size of war plants, along with the number of workers, increased dramatically. Of more significance was the U.S. Army's dispatching of General George S. Patton to the

El Segundo factory produced for Roosevelt's "arsenal of democracy."

lower Mojave Desert to train an army to confront German Field Marshal Erwin Rommel and his feared Afrika Corps. Eventually Patton would drill a force of nearly a million men in the sprawling 162,000-square-mile Desert Training Center that was bisected by the Colorado River Aqueduct.

The vast, blazing desert that had challenged aqueduct surveyors and builders was the perfect practice battlefield for untested soldiers and equipment. It had everything Patton required for his army except water. And Metropolitan would furnish that. When the general arrived at the Iron Mountain Pumping Plant in early 1942, he had already met with Metropolitan's operations and maintenance chief, Robert Diemer, who agreed to cooperate with him. Metropolitan established 15 locations along the aqueduct where the army could draw the water as needed. In addition, power and telephone service were provided to the general through Metropolitan's own desert network. The army that Patton would shape with his sharp tongue and rugged training regimen began mustering in the desert by mid-1942. As many as 200,000 soldiers and support personnel occupied the Desert Training Center at a time. Those who served there soon came to call it "the place that God forgot."

Life in the desert under Patton's hand was harsh. Wearing his trademark

General George S. Patton in Africa: Southern California training had paved the way.

pearl-handled revolver on his right hip, he imposed strict discipline and hardship. There were no luxuries; boot camp seemed like kindergarten by comparison. Soldiers lived in tents under conditions similar to those they soon would encounter in North Africa. At first, despite access to the aqueduct, Patton's entire army only had one "shower" — a huge affair set up near Iron Mountain where 500 soldiers at a time would be trucked in to clean up.

"Old Blood and Guts," as Patton was called by some, was blunt and direct. Larry Green, who worked with the general to set up the water system, recalled that it was impossible to misinterpret him. One day when they were inspecting a well that Metropolitan was digging, a number of bees from nearby hives got underneath the general's field glasses. "It was tough to tell who was madder, the bees or Patton. He told me in no uncertain terms to tell the owner to get the hives out of there or he'd blow them up with a 75 mm gun," Green remembered.

"Living with the Army" created a few minor problems. Patton's tanks tore up patrol roads and sometimes tumbled over embankments into the aqueduct. Power service was interrupted twice when airplanes took down transmission lines, and more than once artillery shells shook up aqueduct maintenance crews, landing within a few hundred feet of workers. Metropolitan had the desert to itself again in 1944 when the Army pulled out.

But there were still welcome reminders of Patton's troops because soldiers buried the supplies they couldn't carry with them. With rationing in effect, workmen such as Gainor Hoover were delighted with the caches they uncovered. "You couldn't believe all the stuff they threw away. I once dug up eight, 100-pound bags of coffee right in the middle of a coffee shortage."

At the outbreak of the war, uneasy Californians didn't know what to expect and were fearful of possible air raids, bombardment or even a Japanese invasion. For a while Metropolitan employees, hired guards and members of the California State Guard patrolled the Colorado River Aqueduct. Major facilities were camouflaged, while out in the desert a big concrete wall, nicknamed the "Burma Wall," was built to shield the electrical transformers at Gene from possible sniper fire. During routine air raid drills and alerts in Southern California, employees at the treatment plant in LaVerne would shut off all the lights including the big red beacon atop the main building. It didn't stay off for long though. Metropolitan quickly received a telephone call from March Air Force Base requesting the beacon be turned back on because it was being used as a navigational landmark at night.

Altar built by Patton's troops near Desert Center

The war wasn't Metropolitan's only concern in the first half of the 1940s. The biggest challenge facing the district was protection of its 1.2 million acre-foot share of Colorado River water. In the mid-'40s, California's allocation twice came under legal and political attack. Metropolitan stood to be the biggest loser if the state's position were not upheld because its rights were junior to those of other public agencies in California. These two instances were the first indications that the water resources of the Colorado might not prove as bountiful as creators of the Colorado River Compact had optimistically forecast.

The first challenge involved Mexico's use of and rights to Colorado River water. Figuratively sitting at the end of a 1,700-mile-long pipeline,

Broadway and 7th in 1940s Los Angeles, the busiest metropolis west of Chicago

Mexico wanted a guaranteed share of the water. That was something the seven squabbling states of the Colorado River basin couldn't abide. They couldn't agree on shares for themselves, let alone one for another country. Their strategy was to offer a minimum amount of water. In 1929, the year the Boulder Canyon Project Act received Congressional approval, the U.S. offered to guarantee Mexico 750,000 acre-feet annually. Though this was the most water Mexico had to that point used in a single year, officials wanted a mind-boggling 3.6 million acre-feet. Negotiations between the two countries collapsed.

Mexico, as well as the United States, benefited from the later development of the Colorado. Completion of Boulder Dam in 1935 and Parker Dam a few years later brought long-sought flood control along the lower river. Releases from the dams ensured a more uniform flow of water and Mexican agriculture flourished on the Colorado delta. By 1941, Mexico's annual usage had jumped to 1.5 million acre-feet, and its government was ready to negotiate again, this time playing one river against another. If the United States, it argued, was unwilling to part with an "equitable" share of the Colorado, whose headwaters it controlled, Mexico would deny water from the Rio Grande, most of which originated in northern Mexico before crossing into Texas. They recognized that Texas citrus farmers in the lower Rio Grande Valley wanted a treaty that would guarantee them water — just as Mexican agriculturists wanted on the Colorado.

Under a cloak of wartime secrecy, an International Boundary and Water Commission began work in 1943 on a treaty covering both rivers. California soon found itself isolated, believing it would lose the most water if Mexico were allotted a large entitlement of the Colorado. Much of that, it reasoned, would come from the so-called "surplus" flows, the 1 million acre-feet of water granted to the lower basin states in the 1922 Colorado River Compact. The other basin states, fearing that Mexico might increase its demands in the future, were willing to give up 1.5 million acre-feet. That amount would not jeopardize their entitlements. Texas Senator Tom

Connally chaired the Senate Foreign Relations Committee which considered the treaty that was hammered out — a treaty that granted Mexico the water it wanted from the Colorado and gave Texas a favorable apportionment of the Rio Grande. California continued to obstruct its final approval by the United States Senate for more than a year. It was a futile delaying action, and the Senate finally ratified the treaty by a 76-10 vote in April 1945.

What ultimately turned out to be a far more serious threat to Metropolitan's Colorado River allotment began in the Arizona state Legislature on February 24, 1944. Seeing their water rights threatened by the impending treaty with Mexico and California's growing use of river water, Arizona's legislators moved swiftly and fatefully. In a single day they passed three measures that shattered the nearly ten years' uneasy peace existing between California and Arizona since the dispute over Parker Dam. In its first action, the Legislature agreed to contract with the federal government for 2.8 million acre-feet from the Colorado, a contract that California disputed. Next, after nearly 22 years of inaction, Arizona finally ratified the 1922 Colorado River Compact. Lastly, the legislators passed a measure allocating $200,000 to conduct surveys for an aqueduct system that would bring water to Phoenix from the Colorado River. Within two years, the Central Arizona Project (CAP) was created as a joint enterprise of Arizona and the federal Bureau of Reclamation.

Cactus guards the Colorado.

California stubbornly resisted. With title to the Colorado's waters still being disputed, the state's Congressional delegation led efforts that repeatedly blocked House approval of legislation that would authorize the CAP. In 1952, Arizona again turned to the U.S. Supreme Court for relief. *Arizona vs. California* was to become the longest and most complicated water case in federal court history. Eleven years would pass before the court would hand down its decision, and aspects of this historical case would remain under litigation in the final decade of this century.

The *Arizona vs. California* ruling would have profound effects upon Metropolitan, but in the years before that judgment would be handed down, other significant events were taking their place in Metropolitan history. During World War II the district made its first annexations in more

No one anticipated the effect America entering the war would have on San Diego's population.

Arizona vs. California *stirred Southland emotions.*

than a decade. First, a number of small Orange County cities united in 1942 to form the Coastal Municipal Water District and join Metropolitan. The second wartime annexation, that of the San Diego County Water Authority, proved far more complicated.

San Diego's long-standing interest in the Colorado River had resulted in its own modest entitlement of 112,000 acre-feet. Before the war, it had considered possible ways it could hook up to the All-American Canal in the Imperial Valley or to the Colorado River Aqueduct to import this water. However, city and county officials had believed existing local supplies would be sufficient through 1950 when the population was expected to reach 260,000. Though there had been speculation as to whether America would enter the war, no one had anticipated the effect that eventuality would have on San Diego's population — a postwar explosion

Northern California snowpack

Metropolitan source: water from the Feather River

Metropolitan source: water from the Colorado River

F. E. Weymouth Filtration Plant in La Verne

The population continues to grow

Wildlife and the Environment: A High-Priority Concern

San Diego in the '90s

Desalination: holding promise for the future

Los Angeles in the '90s

Metropolitan's W.P. Whitsett Intake Pumping Plant on Lake Havasu

Colorado River Aqueduct

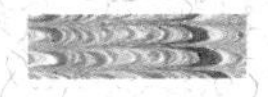

The Sacramento-San Joaquin Delta

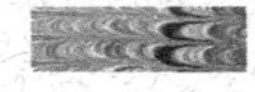

Recreation in the Antioch area of the delta

Drinking water for today and for their future . . .

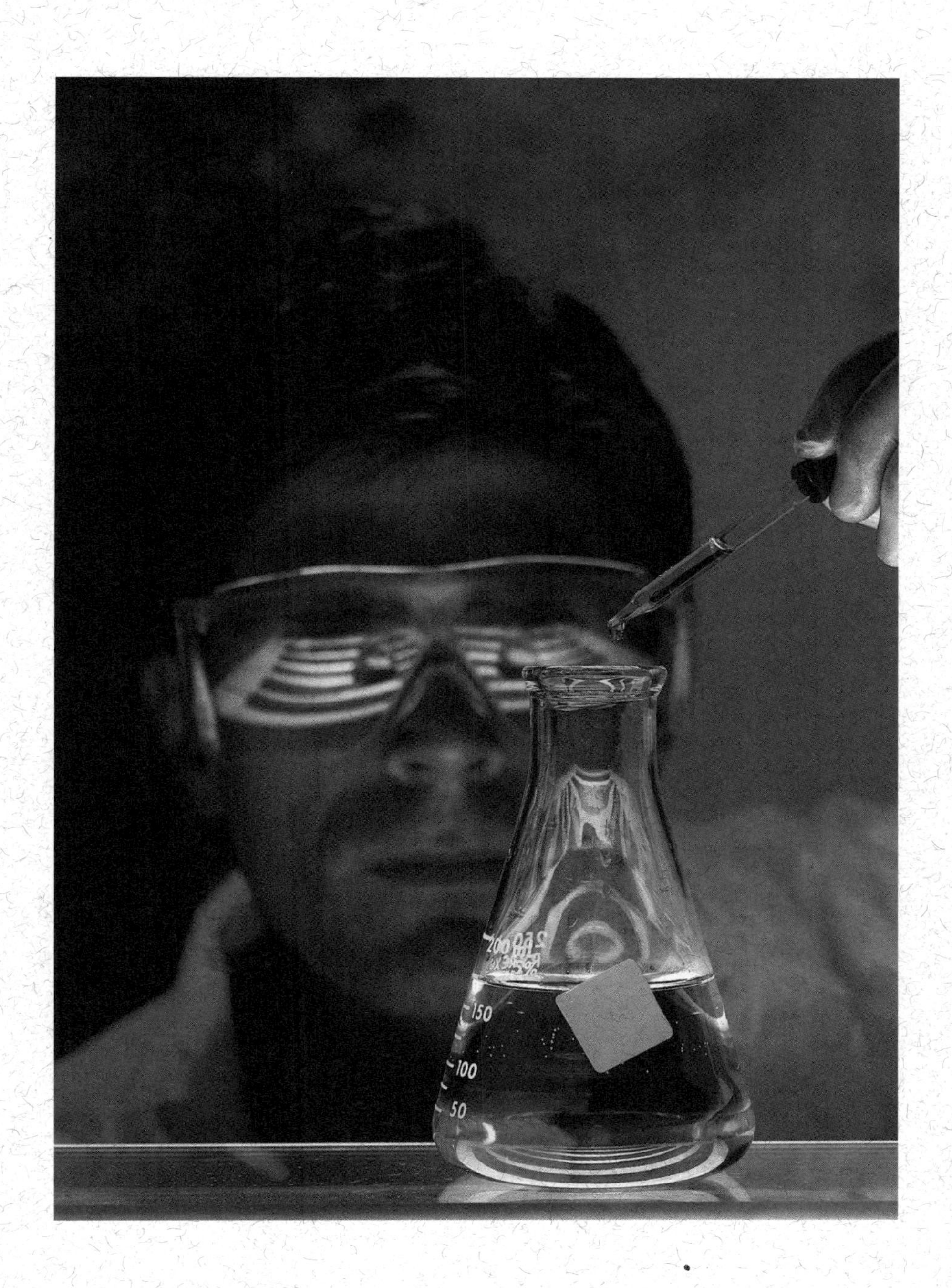

. . . MUST MEET TOUGH STANDARDS.

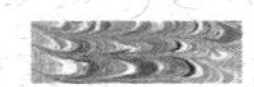

On the Metropolitan horizon: the Domenigoni Valley reservoir
— a conceptual rendering

unlike anything they had ever seen. The 1950 projection was surpassed early in the war, and that didn't include the thousands of servicemen stationed at military bases in the county. As water supplies dwindled, the water authority was formed in 1944. Fearing it would lack sufficient water for its bases, the Navy appealed to President Roosevelt, and eventually a presidential committee proposed the construction of a new federal canal to link San Diego and the Colorado River Aqueduct. When the president authorized the canal as a war project, San Diego was directed to negotiate with Metropolitan for water, a prospect that appealed to neither party.

World War II brought a new look to San Diego.

"San Diego had its own water supply and many thought we could make arrangements other than joining Metropolitan," observed Bill Jennings, who was the legal counsel for the water authority during its negotiations with Metropolitan and the federal government. "Some talked of utilizing local rivers, but that wasn't feasible. By the time of the annexation election, the reality of the situation had hit most people. It was either join or ration."

In post-war Burbank, mushrooming numbers of students made a second high school necessary before the end of the decade.

Metropolitan felt the federal government was twisting its arm to annex San Diego. "The government decided to build the line without asking anybody. It relied on its war powers to force any type of action it saw fit to get the water," said Robert Skinner, who was then a negotiator for Metropolitan.

But before a deal could be hammered out, World War II ended. With the onset of peace the federal government's interest in a San Diego aqueduct evaporated, but although it pulled out, the need for the project still existed. San Diego officials continued their efforts to secure a federal agreement to build the project. Under this plan, the Navy, which still would be one of the largest beneficiaries, would construct the aqueduct and the water authority would pay the $15 million price tag over a 30-year period. Still unresolved was the question of annexation. There were those both at Metropolitan and in San Diego who were opposed.

Eventually a compromise was forged, with Victor Rossetti, a member of Metropolitan's board of directors representing Los Angeles, and Fred Heilbron, a visionary San Diego water leader, its principal authors. The agreement called for the two water agencies to divide construction costs and for Metropolitan to operate the northern half of the pipeline. San Diego agreed to grant its 112,000 acre-foot annual entitlement to Colorado River water to Metropolitan and pay the standard annexation fee — back taxes plus interest, as if it had been a member agency since Metropolitan's organization in 1928. In future years — 1954, 1960 and 1971 — additional pipelines were built to provide still more water to a rapidly-growing San Diego. But none were as welcome as the initial connection in 1947: San Diego was within two weeks of instituting water rationing.

Southern California subdivision under construction: a familiar site in the early '50s

Southern California's post-war era confounded demographers as the population continued to increase rather than diminish as had been predicted. In 1948, the West Basin Municipal Water District was annexed just as a new seven-year dry cycle struck Southern California. As groundwater basins were overdrawn again and other supplies began to run low, new areas looked toward Metropolitan and the Colorado River as the answer to their water problems. Metropolitan's board of directors, however, was becoming cautious about new annexations. Some board members wondered whether the aqueduct would be able to service new as well as existing member agencies. Additionally, as the dispute with Arizona flared up, some feared the deterioration of California's and Metropolitan's water rights on the Colorado River. So, in 1949, MWD directors voted a moratorium on annexations.

Understandably unhappy with this moratorium were those water districts eager to annex. Jumping into the fray, the state Legislature threatened to amend the 1927 Metropolitan Water District Act to permit municipal water districts to join Metropolitan without the approval of its board of directors. Metropolitan altered its stand and came up with a policy requiring newly annexed areas to pay interest on unpaid annexation payments. This provided financial stability and allowed the board to lift the moratorium even though the crucial question regarding water rights remained unanswered.

A new wave of municipal water district annexations followed: Pomona Valley (which later was renamed Three Valleys) in 1950; Eastern, Chino Basin and Orange County in 1951; Foothill in 1953, and Central Basin and Western of Riverside County in 1954. In the 1960s, they were joined by three more municipal water districts — Las Virgenes in 1960, Calleguas in 1961 and Upper San Gabriel Valley in 1963. Metropolitan's last member, the city of San Fernando, joined in 1971 after the Sylmar earthquake left it a city without water, graphically demonstrating its extreme vulnerability. By 1950, Metropolitan had grown far beyond the size and scope envisioned by its founders. Population within its service area had doubled in the first 20-plus years of the district's existence, and the service area itself had tripled in the initial 10 years of Colorado River Aqueduct operation. Metropolitan was outgrowing its facilities and it was time for expansion to keep pace with the robust Southern California economy.

An initially modest expansion program, proposed in 1951, called for $52 million to add two new pumps at each of the pumping plants along the aqueduct and new distribution lines to serve newly annexed areas. Within five years, the size of the job had almost quadrupled to $200 million to cover everything from major expansions of the aqueduct and distribution system to construction of a new headquarters building. Metropolitan's staff had outgrown the quaint Million Dollar Theater building, next to the Grand Central Market at 3rd and Broadway in downtown Los Angeles. It was there that 30 years of water policy and engineering decisions were made to accommodate Southern California's growth.

The expansion was to be financed by revenue from bond sales. A small amount of money was still available from the original aqueduct construction bond election of 1931. The bulk would be generated by selling short-term bonds on annexation fees which would be coming to Metropolitan in the near future. These new bonds were promoted as Proposition W and the public overwhelmingly supported them by an 11-1 margin on June 5, 1956.

Headquarters for Metropolitan for 30 years, the ornate structure at Broadway and 3rd dates back well before this circa 1920 photo.

Munson Dowd, who was in charge of the structural design section during the expansion period and later became chief engineer, explained the landslide passage of the bond issue. "People didn't question the need for water in those days. They knew that this is hot, dry country, that we need outside water, and they were willing to stick their necks out and pay for it."

Passage of Proposition W allowed Metropolitan to enlarge the Colorado River Aqueduct to its full design capacity of 1 billion gallons of water a day. Thirty new pumps, six at each desert plant, were required along with additional siphon and delivery-line capacity. Eighty-four miles of new power transmission lines had to be strung from Hoover (previously Boulder) Dam to provide the energy that would run the new pumps. Closer to home, 165 miles of new pipelines and tunnels were needed in Southern California to bring water to the annexed areas and key existing facilities had to be upgraded. The treatment plant in La Verne, now named after Frank Weymouth, Metropolitan's first general manager, was enlarged to double its capacity. In Riverside County, Lake Mathews, the

Additional delivery line being added at Colorado River Aqueduct intake pumping plant

aqueduct's terminal reservoir that was named to honor Metropolitan's initial general counsel, W. B. Mathews, was enlarged almost 50 percent to 182,000 acre-feet. Other additions to the system during the expansion included Garvey Reservoir in Monterey Park, the second pipeline to San Diego and a second treatment plant, this one to serve a mushrooming Orange County.

Even as the first elements of the expansion were being built, the course envisioned by Metropolitan's water planners was being deflected. The complex issues of *Arizona vs. California* finally were being considered by the courts, with Metropolitan's share of the use of Colorado River water at stake. Meanwhile, an even more ambitious project than the district's Colorado River Aqueduct had been proposed to supply water to many different parts of California. Initially, Metropolitan would stoutly oppose the embryonic State Water Project, only later to embrace it fervently as a solution to many water problems statewide.

A growing San Francisco: eventually its water would have to be imported from the western Sierra.

Chapter 8

OTHER NEEDS, OTHER SYSTEMS

Bold and ambitious, the State Water Project would culminate nearly a century of work performed to address the complicated and conflicting water needs of a complex state. It was born out of the need to balance natural inequities as well as those created by California's varied development. It was, by no means, the first attempt to address the state's water problems in a comprehensive manner. For more than a century, visionary approaches to solve the state's water issues have been outlined and for the most part ignored, left to gather dust until the next study briefly resurrected some portions of its predecessor.

> FOR THE MOST PART, CALIFORNIA HAS BURGEONED FAR FROM ITS SOURCES OF PLENTIFUL WATER.

Perhaps this occurred because California was bequeathed such a cornucopia of resources: some of the world's richest, most fertile soil; an equable Mediterranean climate that nurtures year-round agriculture; deep natural harbors and bays; gold, oil and other mineral wealth; an abundance of rivers and streams, and a majestic landscape of giant mountains and trees, solitary deserts and windswept seascapes. California seemingly has everything its people require — with the significant exception of dependable supplies of water.

Yet, generally speaking, California possesses enough water resources to match its needs. However, this supply usually isn't available *when* and *where* it can be put to beneficial use. The pueblos, missions and towns created by the state's European and American founders didn't require the extensive amounts of water used by today's megacities, megaindustries and megafarms. For the most part, California has burgeoned far from its sources of plentiful water. What would become great cities were founded next to spacious harbors, in vast fertile valleys and on wide coastal plains. The Sierra Nevada and coastal mountain ranges, attracting most of the rain and snow that falls on the state, were distant landmarks. The innumerable streams and rivers that drain those mountains were also, for the most part, bypassed when cities were taking root.

As if inspired by the Franciscan fathers, who founded San Diego in 1769

Northern stream of plenty

and built the first crude waterworks, this practice became the norm in California. Major cities — San Francisco, Los Angeles, Oakland, San Diego, San Jose — as well as their satellite communities, all have had to search far afield for sufficient water. Likewise, California's unrivaled fields, orchards and vineyards in the Sacramento, San Joaquin, Imperial, Coachella and Santa Clara valleys all came to be productive, green oases by a similar imported-water transfusion.

The Mediterranean tradition of building waterworks, which the Franciscans introduced, is a concept that meshes perfectly with California's geography and climate. Complex systems for storing and moving water became inevitable because it is a resource that is both plentiful and scarce. In any given year, California receives more than enough rain and snow to meet its water needs. Unfortunately, most precipitation falls far from where it is needed and can be used: About three-quarters falls in the northern third of the state. The demand for water, however, is virtually the opposite: About three-quarters is consumed in the lower two-thirds of the state.

California's climate adds a final and capricious element to this mix. Historically, extremes of drought and flood have plagued the state. At times, calls for flood control facilities have been as loud and persistent as cries for water development. Annual precipitation fluctuates to such a degree that the term "average rainfall" is almost a misnomer. For example, torrential flooding in the winter of 1861-62 turned the floor of the Sacramento Valley into a vast inland sea. In contrast, a severe three-year drought that stunned the land began a few hundred miles to the south the following winter and by the time it was over, Southern California's cattle-ranching economy had withered into near-extinction.

Faced with the contrasting examples of the Chumash and the Gabrielino Indians on the one hand and the Franciscans on the other, Californians have copied the latter in an effort to assure themselves a reliable supply of water. To achieve this, individuals, companies, cities, regions, state government and the federal government all have looked to the watersheds and rivers of California to balance an illusion of availability with the reality of water needs. Giant networks of dams, canals, pipelines, aqueducts and pumping plants have been erected to carry water to where it was needed throughout the state while also providing life-saving flood control measures where required.

The modern era of California's water development dates back nearly 150 years to Gold Rush days and early statehood. From the very beginning, water and gold were inextricably linked. The first nuggets of gold that James Marshall plucked out of the tailrace of Sutter's mill in 1848 were glistening with the moisture of the American River. In the years that followed, powerful jets of water were necessary for freeing most of the gold from the granite grasp of the Mother Lode.

Before the water projects, Yuba City was prone to floods.

The state's preeminent city at the dawn of the Gold Rush was San Francisco, which until then had been able to rely on local springs and streams for its water. But the discovery of gold turned San Francisco into a mecca, attracting gold seekers from around the world, and the city soon found itself short of water. But entrepreneurial merchants quickly devised a profitable solution: They shipped inland water across San Francisco Bay in barrels and delivered it door-to-door in wagons. Much later, water historians would call this enterprise "the first example of transporting water from one watershed to another in California." Certainly, it was an example that San Francisco and other communities would remember and duplicate on a far more elaborate scale in future decades.

When California's first Legislature met in Sacramento in 1850, the issue of water was high on its agenda. A surveyor general was directed to plan improvements in internal navigation, drainage and irrigation throughout the state. Unfortunately, nothing was done to implement proposals as

IN THE FRENZY TO FIND GOLD, ENTIRE MOUNTAINSIDES WERE WASHED AWAY. THE DESTRUCTION WAS AS AWESOME AS THE PROFITS WERE GREAT.

Hydraulic mining: the destruction was awesome.

Californians were too preoccupied with prospecting for the gold hidden in the Sierra Nevada.

There were enormous treasure troves of gold to be found, but most of it was buried among tons of rock, sand and gravel on river bottoms or bound up in the earth. Few miners actually struck it rich prospecting with a pan or pick. But by 1853, they had found a way to harness the power of water to help them separate gold from its mineral chaff. The technique was called hydraulic mining and it enabled miners to move mountains to get to gold. Powerful streams of water were directed through hose nozzles to wash away the top layer of Sierra Nevada hillsides. Slurry ran into wooden sluice boxes, where the heavier gold easily could be separated from the tailings that were dumped back into rivers and streams. In the frenzy to feed the sluice boxes and find gold, entire mountainsides were washed away and riverbanks undercut. The destruction was as awesome as the profits were great.

The hungry nozzles of the hydraulic miners inevitably led to water development and disputes. As more and more water was required, grand works were fashioned to capture and direct it. Streams and rivers were dammed to create storage so the miners weren't at the mercy of nature's irregular flows. Tinker-toy-like wooden flumes were fashioned to transport water down from the high country and thousands of miles of ditches and canals dug to carry it directly to miners' hoses. Ultimately, it was the debris swept downstream that triggered the activity that would put a halt to the destruction upstream. Riverbeds became clogged, adding to the danger of winter and spring flooding; navigation on the Sacramento River frequently was impeded; and muddy debris oozed over undermined levees built to protect newly-established farms.

It finally took action by the federal government and federal courts to end this detrimental form of mining. The U.S. Army Corps of Engineers, which was responsible for maintaining navigation on the Sacramento River, filed suit against the miners. Farmers, who had discovered the productivity of Sacramento Valley soil, supported the suit. In 1884, federal Judge Lorenzo Sawyer all but killed hydraulic mining in his decision in the case of *Woodruff vs. North Bloomfield.* It outlawed hydraulic mining in all areas that were tributary to the Sacramento River unless the mining companies constructed dams to trap debris. Few of the companies were willing to take on this new financial burden, particularly since the goldfields were beginning to play out. Three decades of unrestrained hydraulic mining were over, and California was already seeking other, more beneficial uses for its water.

In 1878, when William Hammond Hall was appointed California's first state engineer, not only was he given the job of determining the damages caused by hydraulic mining, but, as had been the surveyor general in 1850, he was asked to prepare studies of the Sacramento and San Joaquin rivers that would uncover ways to improve navigation, promote drainage and provide for irrigation. Filled with curiosity and a thirst for knowledge, "Ham" Hall, as he liked to be called, was the perfect man for the job.

During the Civil War he had served as a field engineer and hydrographer with the Corps of Engineers before moving west. Prior to his appointment as state engineer he had already made significant contributions to California by developing what is now Golden Gate Park while employed as San Francisco's engineer and superintendent of parks.

Hall's interest in water quickly spread beyond the banks of the Sacramento and San Joaquin rivers, as he voiced his concern about the water resources of the entire state. Up to that time, remarkably little was known about California's resources. Hall dispatched survey parties to systematically map and measure the state's streams and rivers and collected sketchy past records of rainfall and stream runoff wherever available. But beyond this, he repeatedly recommended in his reports to the Legislature that the state undertake irrigation and drainage projects. Many of the works and studies he proposed marked Hall as a man a generation or more ahead of his time. Yet his passion for regional water planning and development ultimately led to his downfall.

Angered by the Legislature's refusal to fund the third volume of his irrigation study and to print a map of California's water resources, Hall resigned in 1888. The Legislature retaliated by abolishing his job. Hall's work and many of the ideas he conceived endured and would be included in Central Valley water projects in the next century.

A dozen years after Hall's resignation, the 20th century ushered in a new era of California water development. First San Francisco, then Los Angeles reached out toward distant rivers. While San Francisco was occupied with tapping the west slope of the Sierra Nevada, Los Angeles' energy was focused on the east slope of the same range.

In 1900, San Francisco began investigating potential sources of water for a population that had swelled to 350,000 and was projected to double or triple in the next half century. The city had clearly begun to outstrip its local water supply, which was provided by the private Spring Valley Water Company.

By the following year, the Tuolumne River, more than 150 miles distant, had emerged as the best choice for a municipal water source. However, this choice was fated to be embroiled in seemingly perpetual controversy. Private power interests were opposed to municipal ownership of public utilities. Local irrigation districts feared losing their water rights to the Tuolumne. But most troublesome of all, individuals and organizations, such as the young Sierra Club, which had been founded in 1892 by naturalist John Muir, vehemently protested San Francisco's plan to dam the Tuolumne River inside the boundaries of Yosemite National Park. The plan called for submerging the Hetch Hetchy Valley, a site regarded as near equal in beauty to Yosemite Valley. Foes of the Hetch Hetchy

Sacramento parade in 1885, in area today known as Old Town

Aqueduct stood stubbornly firm as the battle for the project's approval raged for more than a decade. In December of 1913, Hetch Hetchy was sanctioned by both houses of Congress. But construction, which began the following year, wasn't concluded for a full 20 years.

By 1934, not only had Los Angeles long since completed its aqueduct from the Owens Valley (in 1913, the year before work on Hetch Hetchy began), but work on the Colorado River Aqueduct was well under way and San Francisco's neighbors across the bay were operating a water system of their own. In 1923, Oakland and eight other communities had united to form the East Bay Municipal Utility District, or East Bay MUD as it has become more familiarly known. The agency was created to siphon another Sierra Nevada river, the Mokelumne, and before the end of the decade the Mokelumne Aqueduct was in service.

O'Shaunessy Dam forming Hetch Hetchy Reservoir, which supplies San Francisco

Completion of these four major aqueducts ended a significant phase of California's water development. It had been an era of diverse cities and municipal water districts building systems to meet their water needs. Though additional systems would be required, their scope would be so broad that only state or federal agencies could build them.

In 1920, the groundwork for such development was laid by Colonel Robert Marshall with a 12-page report published by the California Irrigation Association. Marshall, chief hydrographer for the U.S. Geological Survey, proposed an ambitious, statewide program of water facilities costing $1 billion. He called for a dam across the upper Sacramento River, a series of additional storage reservoirs, irrigation canals descending both flanks of the Sacramento and San Joaquin valleys, and the diversion of the Kern River from the San Joaquin Valley into Southern California. The colonel's proposal became known as the Marshall Plan. In an eloquent exhortation that challenged Californians, he wrote:

"...The people of California, indifferent to the bountiful gifts that nature

Dedication lunch atop Pardee Dam on the Mokelumne River, 1929: to provide a water supply for Oakland and surrounding communities

OAKLAND AND EIGHT OTHER COMMUNITIES HAD UNITED TO SIPHON ANOTHER SIERRA NEVADA RIVER, THE MOKELUMNE.

has given them, sit idly by waiting for rain, indefinitely postponing irrigation and allowing every year millions and millions of dollars in water to pour unused into the sea.... There in the Sacramento and San Joaquin valleys combined in one immense tract, lies the largest, richest, and most fertile body of indifferently used or unused land in the United States — perhaps the world. I have read the interesting statements of able engineers that say it is not feasible to take the waters from the Sacramento Valley into the San Joaquin Valley, but notwithstanding all the authorities I say it is entirely feasible. It must be done and it will be done.... Remember... that the plan is a big, statewide plan, and also remember that success, as California measures success, is assured only when the enterprise is planned and carried out in its entirety. The plan herewith presented is based upon common sense as well as science...and the entire scheme can be finished and in full operation with assured success in 10 years."

The Central Valley Project was under way in 1942 with the construction of Shasta Dam.

Marshall's plan didn't have a prayer of acceptance or implementation in the 1920s. The sheer magnitude of his proposal put off members of the Legislature. But many of his ideas were sound and would be incorporated into future California water resources planning. Elements of Marshall's thinking were apparent in the State Water Plan of 1931, a document which culminated 10 years of studying the state's water resources. Interestingly, this plan was the first such effort completed since the days of Ham Hall in the 1880s. Though its author, state engineer Edward Hyatt, like Marshall, had a statewide vision, he targeted the needs of the Sacramento and San Joaquin valleys.

Hyatt, as had Marshall, proposed damming the Sacramento River, calling for the construction of Shasta Dam. Other elements of the new plan included additional reservoirs to provide for flood control and water storage, hydroelectric plants to generate power, and pumping plants in the Sacramento-San Joaquin Delta, along with a network of irrigation canals to furnish the San Joaquin Valley with water. Hyatt's plan proved to be the backbone for what became known as the Central Valley Project. In 1933,

Processing San Joaquin Valley sugar beet harvest at Visalia factory

that project sailed through the California Legislature, followed by voter endorsement to the tune of a $170 million bond issue that promised to cover initial costs.

The Central Valley Project, however, was not fated to be built by the state. California was unable to sell water bonds as the weight of the Depression spread across the United States and sapped the nation's economy. Then in 1935, President Roosevelt cleared the way for the project to be taken over by the federal Bureau of Reclamation by authorizing the use of emergency relief funds.

These emergency monies enabled ground to be broken in 1937 on the Contra Costa Canal, the first unit of the Central Valley Project, and the following year construction began on Shasta Dam. The outbreak of World War II delayed work as did post-war revisions to the original plan. It wasn't until 1951 that water from the Central Valley Project first reached the San Joaquin Valley. Even as work had continued on the primarily agricultural CVP, California faced other pressing water issues. Clearly, the time had come to put together a water project that was truly statewide in scope and impact.

BROWN BECAME A CRUSADER, USING THE PULPIT OF THE GOVERNORSHIP TO SELL EDMONSTON'S PLAN TO THE STATE LEGISLATURE AND THEN TO CALIFORNIA'S VOTERS.

The Feather River

Chapter 9

THE BATTLE FOR APPROVAL

Water and politics often don't mix. They can be a volatile, combustive combination. This certainly was true during the 1950s and the early 1960s as California grappled to keep abreast of the changes that were sweeping the landscape. Many of these changes revolved around the issue of growth as California continued on its inexorable path toward becoming the most populous state.

No one could dispute the multitude of water problems at the mid-century mark. But one could get a bucketful of arguments about what or who caused those problems, what should be done about them and who should fix them. A north-south sectionalism emerged as water became politicized along geographic lines, and by the mid-1950s strains of a "Don't-let-them-take-our-water" battle cry were being heard in Northern California.

Out of the seeming confusion of this time came an answer designed to solve some of California's water problems — the State Water Project. While thousands of people would be involved with the project from its inception through its construction, it is to a strong degree the product of two men, Governor Edmund G. "Pat" Brown and A.D. Edmonston. These two Northern Californians were ideally suited for the times and daunting tasks they would face. Edmonston, the state engineer, built on the foundation created by his predecessors — Ham Hall, Robert Marshall and Edward Hyatt — when he conceived of what he called the Feather River Project in 1950. Later in the decade, Brown, realizing the imperative need for water development, became a crusader, using the pulpit of the governorship to sell Edmonston's plan to the state Legislature and then to California's voters.

The Feather River Project — which would in time become the State Water Project — was conceived to address a variety of water concerns, largely fueled by the growing population. In the two-decade span of the 1940s and '50s, California's population more than doubled, growing from 6.9 million to 15.7 million. In Southern California, the focus of much of the state's growth, additional water was needed for the newly born, the legions of transplanted residents and burgeoning new industries. In Central California's San Joaquin Valley, millions of acres of fertile land awaited supplies of irrigation water. At the same time, other regions of the valley faced problems caused by overpumping of underground basins. In Northern California, the peninsula south of San Francisco had become a prime growth area badly in need of water transfusions. So much water had been pumped out of underground basins that portions of downtown San Jose and other areas in the Santa Clara Valley had subsided by a dozen feet. And almost everywhere in the state, from the flood plain of the Los Angeles River to small towns bordering Sierra Nevada streams, communities were exposed to the unpredictable and deadly threat of flooding. Clearly, California had an acute need for flood control as well as additional water supplies.

Despite the pressing problems, progress in the direction of Edmonston's plan was being made — some would say at a snail's pace — during the post-war years. In the early 1940s, controversy had lingered over the assumption by the federal government of the Central Valley Project and the slow pace of its completion. By the end of World War II, a backlog of projects proposed by the Bureau of Reclamation and Army Corps of Engineers had developed, along with a state-federal rivalry over who should build flood-control works. In 1945, a Corps of Engineers report called for flood-control facilities on the middle and north forks of the Feather River, a tributary of the Sacramento. A California plan, prepared by state engineer Edward Hyatt, proposed a dam farther downstream on the main stem of the Feather, near the town of Oroville. Eventually, this led to an agreement that California's next major flood-control dam would be built on the Feather River.

But by 1951 when this project hadn't been realized, a pair of rival water development plans emerged. One was a rather grandiose federal Bureau of Reclamation proposal; the other was Edmonston's blueprint for the

Additional water was needed for the already-born, the soon-to-be-born and the houses being built for their families.

Feather River. The federal plan was regional in scope, spanning the area from the state's water-rich north coast to Southern California's deserts and the state of Nevada. Among the Bureau of Reclamation's ideas were plans for diverting water from the Klamath River on the north coast into the Central Valley; taking water from another Sacramento tributary, the American, into Nevada; and making water deliveries from the Los Angeles Aqueduct into the Mojave Desert. Edmonston's plan covered nearly as much territory — from Northern California south almost to the Mexican border — and had several clear advantages over the federal proposal. It was entirely within California, so it could be built by the state without federal participation, and it didn't require approval by another state government as did the bureau's plan.

More importantly, Edmonston got the jump on the federal government. His plan, which became known as the Feather River Project, was completed first and presented to the state Legislature in 1951. From that point on, the federal plan didn't have a chance, while Edmonston's project received additional funding for continued planning. As presented, it called for building Oroville Dam on the Feather River to provide flood control, water storage and hydroelectric power. The water captured would be released and eventually exported from the Sacramento-San Joaquin Delta via a number of aqueducts leading to the San Francisco Bay area, the San Joaquin Valley and Southern California.

Edmonston had moved quickly and decisively to introduce the Feather River Project. Although the original proposal was drafted in just under six months, it was not a rashly conceived idea. Rather it was the crowning achievement of a long and eventful career as a civil servant. "He had been thinking about it for a long while, and when the time was right he moved on it," said his son, Robert Edmonston, an engineer himself who also worked to create the State Water Project. "It would become an obsession with him."

A.D. Edmonston

Edmonston had first come to work in the state engineer's office in 1925, filling a temporary vacancy. He wound up staying three decades during which he helped Edward Hyatt develop the 1931 State Water Plan, created the Feather River Project and then the 1957 California Water Plan. Edmonston cut an imposing figure, standing 6' 1" and weighing 270 pounds. However, his weight was a burden as one of his legs had been crushed in a construction accident. Each day, he had to bind the leg from ankle to thigh and walk with the aid of custom-made shoes. When his career as a construction engineer was cut short by the accident, this son of the north coast went to work for the state where he would make an indelible mark.

"He was a visionary, but a practical man," recalled John Teerink, a former director of the state Department of Water Resources who was a junior engineer under Edmonston. "I remember going to his office in 1950 and his telling us what he had in mind — pumping water down the San Joaquin Valley, over the Tehachapis and all the way to Horsethief Canyon near the Mexican border. What was really new was pumping over the Tehachapis, and when I heard it I viewed it with considerable awe and skepticism. But Edmonston knew California geography and hydrology like the palm of his hand, and he told us where the key points were to be."

Edmonston masterminded the proposal for the Feather River Project in three steps. First he outlined the project for his staff; second, he gave

Teerink the task of committing the plan to paper, siting all of the necessary facilities; and finally, accompanied by Teerink or another engineer — and upon occasion by his wife — he double-checked everything along his proposed route. "My father laid out the project, the essence of what we have today, from an automobile," explained Robert Edmonston. "He would get out, shuffle around, get back in the car and drive down the valley, all the while mapping out the aqueduct on quad sheets."

Harvey O. Banks

Edmonston's last five years of his public service were consumed with completion of another report that would substantiate the engineering and financial feasibility of his plan. This resulted in only minor modifications to Edmonston's original idea. Provision was made for more service to the San Francisco Bay area and for more water storage capacity with the addition of San Luis Reservoir in the San Joaquin Valley. By the end of 1955, an independent engineering firm, the Bechtel Corporation, evaluated Edmonston's final proposal and endorsed its engineering soundness and economic feasibility. But by then Edmonston had retired, and it would be up to others to convince the Legislature, the voters and even water agencies such as Metropolitan that the project should be built.

In 1956, Governor Goodwin Knight created a new Department of Water Resources as a central agency to handle the state's water business and named Harvey Banks as its founding director. Banks, like Edmonston, was a respected engineer. His forte was political diplomacy. He was effective working for both a Democrat and a Republican governor and his talent for creating consensus and compromise would play a significant role in keeping the project moving in the politically trying years ahead.

The new department's first achievement was the completion of a comprehensive study of the state's water resources and needs that had been requested by the Legislature in 1947. Two-thirds of the job had been finished earlier in the decade. The final portion, known as the California Water Plan, outlined a broad picture of the state's future water needs, as

IN SACRAMENTO, BATTLE LINES WERE DRAWN ON A NORTH-SOUTH BASIS.

well as detailing the immediate, crucial need for the Feather River Project. Proposing that a series of projects be built in stages to match the state's growth until it had reached maximum development, the California Water Plan enumerated 376 new reservoirs and related facilities which could be constructed over the ensuing 100 years. It pinpointed the Feather River Project as its first unit and reiterated the need to finance and build it with all due speed.

Rapid startup of the project proved impossible, however, as it became lost in a political labyrinth. In Sacramento, battle lines were drawn on a north-south basis. In Southern California, members of Metropolitan's board of directors — particularly chairman Joseph Jensen — remained unconvinced that the Feather River Project was the best solution. They initiated the exploration of options for MWD building its own aqueduct. Metropolitan focused on the Eel River, and in 1959, two engineers, Henry J. "Hank" Mills (later to become a Metropolitan general manager)

The Eel River

and George Archibald, were dispatched to investigate possible routes for an aqueduct leading from the water-rich North Coast to Southern California. Ultimately, the two engineers and an independent report from the Bechtel Corporation reached identical conclusions: While it certainly was possible from an engineering standpoint to build a system from the Eel River, politically it was out of the question. No single water agency, particularly one from Southern California, could hope to build a massive water system from one end of the state to the other. If there were to be such a system, the state would have to build it.

But the prospects of that being realized seemed remote in the late 1950s. Three times — in 1956, 1957 and 1958 — the Knight administration tried and failed to win support for the Feather River Project in the state Legislature. The strategy had been to draft an amendment to the state constitution that would satisfy the conflicting desires of water interests from border to border. Northern California demanded guarantees that it would have a future water supply when needed, based on the "counties of origin" section of the state water code. In addition, the north sought money to assist in developing local water projects as compensation for losing some of what it considered *its* water. There were demands from the southern half of the state as well. The most important of these was a guarantee that some future Legislature could not take action that would violate project water delivery contracts and restrict water to Northern California. These differences couldn't be mediated and the prospects of passing any statewide water bill seemed bleak. The state Senate had not yet been reapportioned on the basis of population and was still dominated by rural northern lawmakers capable of defeating any measure.

The stalemate seemed unresolvable until Pat Brown entered the picture. Elected in the fall of 1958, Brown occupied the governor's mansion with a conviction that California had to solve its water problems and a determination to snap the legislative deadlock. His appreciation of water issues was genuine and inbred. The son of Colusa County farmers in the

Sacramento Valley, Brown grew up in a family that had a fruit orchard and raised wheat and barley. Water was a constant concern and his mother told him they "used to regularly pray for rain." Later Brown would study both water and mining law and he thought it a portent of things to come when the California Law Review devoted an entire issue to water law the day he was elected state attorney general in 1950.

Former governor, Edmund G. "Pat" Brown, reflects on hard-driving days of 1959 and 1960.

In reviewing his long years in public service, Brown considered the State Water Project his most significant achievement. "I knew the state was growing," he reflected years later. "Everywhere I looked we needed water and that water had to be transported because it wasn't available where the people were. I realized we had to build the Feather River Project and put my muscle behind it. The project needed a crusader and I feel my initiative and refusal to permit anything to delay it were decisive. It took everything I had to get the Feather River Project through the Legislature."

In early 1959, Brown assembled a five-man team to aid him in developing a new strategy to break the Sacramento impasse and ramrod a Feather River bill through the Legislature. The plan developed largely through the work of Brown; Harvey Banks, then director of the Department of Water Resources, whom the Democratic governor had retained from his Republican predecessor to gain bipartisan support; Ralph Brody, a Sacramento lawyer specializing in water and power law who left private practice to become special counsel on water matters to the governor and would the following year begin a 17-year stint as manager-chief counsel of Westlands Water District in the Central Valley; and B. Abbott Goldberg, a former deputy attorney general under Brown who had provided him with advice on water matters and whom the governor would in 1966 appoint to the Superior Court bench, where he would serve for 12 years before stepping down to become scholar in residence at McGeorge School of Law. The two men who would lend their names to the bill that would authorize the Feather River Project and skillfully maneuver it through the

Legislature were Hugh Burns, the Democratic Senate leader, and Carley Porter, Democratic chairman of the Assembly Water Committee.

Senator Hugh Burns

Their plan discarded attempts to amend the state constitution. Instead, assurances sought by the north and south were embodied in a bond measure to finance the Feather River Project. That measure — the Burns-Porter Act — had to win approval of the Legislature and subsequently be ratified by the voters of California. Most of the money for the water project would be realized from the sale of $1.75 billion in general obligation bonds which would be repaid with revenue from the sale of water and power created by the project. Additional funds would be realized through the creation of a State Water Fund, which would be loaned some of the existing and future royalties the state collected from tidelands oil leases. However, unlike most uses made of tidelands money, the funds for the water project would be repaid with interest.

Assemblyman Carley Porter

The Burns-Porter Act also contained regional guarantees including the maintaining of existing water rights in the areas of origin upon which the north had insisted. About $130 million that would be generated from the sale of bonds would be earmarked for building local water projects by public agencies, primarily in Northern California. San Joaquin Valley's and Southern California's previously voiced fears of having this source of water cut off by future legislative action were quelled with the provision that their water contracts could not be cancelled during the lifetime of the bonds. And with an eye to the future, the Burns-Porter Act also contained a provision that would allow the future construction of other water facilities when needed.

When their proposal was complete, Brown and his advisors didn't shy away from confrontation. They opened the struggle to pass the Burns-Porter Act in the state Senate with its corps of opposition from rural northern counties. "We knew it was going to be more difficult in the Senate, but we wanted to clear that hurdle first," said Brown. "It was the bitterest fight of my political career and it took all the political muscle I could use, everything I had, to convince senators to vote for it."

Stubborn opponents managed to pass a number of minor changes to the bill, but an estimated 50 other amendments which would have gutted the Burns-Porter Act were defeated. The battle ended in June 1959 with a 25-12 vote authorizing the Feather River Project. When the battleground shifted to the Assembly, the governor's team shrewdly decided to block any amendments to the bill it had just shepherded through the Senate. If they succeeded, they wouldn't have to go back to the Senate to reconcile the differences in the two bills. With Porter directing the floor fight and Brown again twisting arms from the governor's office, amendment after amendment was defeated and by the end of June, the Burns-Porter Act was approved by a 50-30 vote.

Pat Brown had won a notable victory in the first six months of his administration, but the battle was far from over. He still had to convince the people of California and Joe Jensen, the skeptical chairman of Metropolitan's board of directors, that the Feather River Project and the Burns-Porter Act deserved their support. Both would prove to be hard sells. In addition, these two concerns soon became enmeshed with another issue, that of securing contracts for the State Water Project.

To ratify the Burns-Porter Act, the measure became Proposition 1 on the November 1960 ballot. A simple majority vote was required to approve the Feather River Project. Meanwhile, the governor's office began establishing guidelines for construction. Among them was a provision specifying that building could not begin until the state had secured contracts for at least 75 percent of the water that would be developed. This would ensure the financial stability of the venture. Passage of Proposition 1 and the gathering of signed contracts thus became linked in a complicated numbers game. The election was bound to be close because of Northern California opposition. The governor and his advisors knew they had to win big in Southern

California if Proposition 1 were to carry. At the same time, the state needed signed contracts and the Brown administration felt it was imperative to negotiate the first one with Metropolitan, whose service area boundaries contained the largest block of potential voters in the state.

Joseph Jensen

In January 1960, a long, difficult series of negotiations between the state and MWD began — an indirect test of wills between the governor and Jensen, who had disagreed with many of the financial and engineering concepts of the plan. Although Metropolitan was to become the State Water Project's largest contractor before the end of the year, Jensen initially stood firm. The longtime chairman of MWD's board of directors held sway over the Los Angeles delegation, the largest on the board, which in turn exerted great influence. A year earlier, the board, at Jensen's prompting, had authorized the study of the Eel River, even though prospects of Metropolitan building an aqueduct from Northern California were regarded by most astute observers as virtually impossible. By early 1960, many of Jensen's earlier doubts about the engineering concepts of the Feather River Project had been satisfied, but the financial issues lingered. Jensen had remained skeptical and Metropolitan's board determined it would not endorse Proposition 1 until a workable contract with the state had been negotiated.

"Joe Jensen was a totally inflexible man and it would take more than an earthquake to move him. He sincerely believed Metropolitan was not getting a fair shake from the contract," declared Robert Skinner, who in 1960 was Metropolitan's assistant general manager and one of its two principal negotiators along with Charles Cooper, the general counsel. Department of Water Resources Director Harvey Banks was the state's chief negotiator and kept in close touch with the governor. Negotiations that dragged on for almost 11 months hammered out an agreement that was expected to be a model for further negotiations with other contractors. As the state's chief negotiator, Banks found himself in a dual role: acting on behalf of

Negotiations between Metropolitan and the state were lengthy...and tough.

the state and on behalf of 30 other public agencies which eventually would sign similar contracts.

These documents would determine how the costs of building and operating the Feather River Project would be divided as well as how much water each agency would receive.

Money was the core issue and many millions of dollars were at stake. Metropolitan wanted each contractor to pay its fair share without a subsidy. The state, however, was more concerned with developing and maintaining a steady cash flow to meet the expenses of the project. Many areas of difference were ironed out during the long negotiating process, but the two parties remained at loggerheads on the question of how much of the project costs agricultural contractors would pay and when they would pay it. Farming areas were financially limited because they weren't yet fully developed. Finally, Metropolitan agreed to a state plan allowing agricultural contractors to pay off their share of the project at a lower rate initially and then pay more in interest in subsequent years as their economic base developed.

Another financial issue fostered disagreement that seemingly defied solution. The Brown administration had adopted a principle that each contractor pay a share of the cost only of those facilities needed to bring water to that agency. Thus, some contractors would have to pay more than others. Metropolitan was one as it was situated at the far end of the aqueduct system and required more pumping plants and miles of canal than did, for example, contractors in the San Joaquin Valley or the San Francisco Bay area.

"This concept was fairly controversial in itself and there was no chance of a post office rate, where everybody paid the same fees for transportation facilities," said Skinner. "It was one of the primary reasons Jensen opposed the contract."

SOME CONTRACTORS WOULD HAVE TO PAY MORE THAN OTHERS. METROPOLITAN WAS ONE.

Given this state-mandated rule, however, negotiations centered around two opposing philosophies for determining costs of facilities and the different ways urban vs. agricultural contractors would take delivery of their water. Metropolitan had the flexibility of receiving its water throughout the year and storing it in reservoirs the state was going to build in Southern California as part of the project. The agricultural contractors, however, wanted most of their entitlement water delivered in the growing season — spring and summer — when it would be used directly on crops. They had no significant storage facilities which meant the aqueduct would have to be considerably larger to handle the peak water demands of the farmers. Because the system would have to be enlarged, Metropolitan, which stood to be the state's largest contractor, wanted transportation charges to be calculated on the basis of aqueduct capacity. The agricultural agencies rejected that notion and countered that the charges should be determined solely on the maximum amount of water a contractor was allowed to draw.

Dragging on through the long summer and into the fall of 1960, contract negotiations took place among representatives of Metropolitan, the state and an unofficial and indirect third party. That "silent partner" was Allen Bottorff, a Kern County farmer who later became one of the founders of the Kern County Water Agency, another contractor of the state project. Bottorff never officially participated in the bargaining, but he always seemed to be in Harvey Banks' Sacramento office. Don Whitlock, of MWD's legal staff, was a member of the negotiating team. He recalled the situation: "We would always run into him [Bottorff] in Sacramento and we even shared cabs from the airport. During our meetings, Banks would occasionally leave the room for a few minutes and then come back to resume work with us. Day after day, Banks would do the same thing. I never saw him talk to Bottorff, but Bottorff certainly did a lot of sitting around in that office."

The Southland was growing rapidly, and contract negotiators fought to obtain the best deal possible for those who largely would pay the costs: the children of the '50s.

Eventually, in October, Skinner suggested a compromise incorporating aqueduct capacity and entitlements by taking an average of the two. Though a number of lesser questions remained to be resolved, there seemed to be agreement on a contract as the election date for Proposition 1 neared. There was one imposing exception — Joe Jensen. Metropolitan's board chairman remained adamantly opposed to the contract and the project. He refused to waver, even under the pressure of telephone calls and telegrams from Pat Brown, who was barnstorming his way around California to gather support for the bonds. Four times in October, Metropolitan's board of directors rejected its staff's and executive committee's recommendations to approve the negotiated contract and, thus, narrowly sustained Jensen.

"Metropolitan's management favored the contract as a matter of practicality," explained Skinner. "There was no possibility of getting a better contract and without our endorsement there was the possibility that the bond issue would not pass. That would have obliterated the project."

On November 1, a scant week before the bond election, Jensen's eroding support crumbled completely when the board met for a fifth time to consider the contract. Two of his allies in the Los Angeles delegation were not present and a third member, Noah Dietrich, declared he was switching his vote and was in favor of the contract. With the loss of three votes, Jensen no longer held the balance of power in the delegation, which voted by the unit rule. And with Dietrich's announcement, more than one-third of the board's votes changed sides, triggering a landslide in which nearly everyone jumped on the pro-contract bandwagon.

Even Southern California's freeway system was growing.

No one can say whether Metropolitan's subsequent late endorsement of the project played a decisive role in the passage of Proposition 1 the following week. Certainly it didn't hurt; the margin of victory was slight. The Feather River Project's most indefatigable proponent was the governor. Brown was stumping for votes all fall, campaigning not only for the water project but also for the presidential campaign of John Fitzgerald Kennedy. Opposition to the bonds was strong, particularly in Northern California where the San Francisco Chronicle lambasted the Feather River Project, calling it a "hoax."

The election on November 8 was a squeaker. More than 5.8 million

President John Fitzgerald Kennedy dedicates Whiskeytown Dam and Reservoir near Redding just two months before that fateful November day in Dallas.

Californians cast ballots, and Kennedy, though he won the presidency, lost California by a mere 35,000 votes. The bonds, however, fared better, winning with a margin of fewer than 200,000 votes. As expected, Northern California voted against Proposition 1. Butte County, where Oroville Dam was slated for construction, turned out to be the only northern county to vote for the bonds. A strong yes vote in Southern California, particularly in San Diego County, overcame northern opposition at the ballot box. The final margin of victory was just 173,944 votes.

A final barrier stood in the way of construction of the water project. The contract hammered out between Metropolitan and the state allowed the Legislature to make changes in the document during its 1961 session. Metropolitan would be permitted 180 days to approve any changes, which in all likelihood would be unacceptable if opponents of the Feather River Project had had anything to do with them. If Metropolitan failed to endorse the amendments, the document would be void. And without the agreement, which was to be the framework for similar contracts with 30 other water agencies, work on the system could be delayed once more. More than 50 amendments were tossed into the Assembly hopper in 1961, covering such concerns as water rights, fish and wildlife protection, the delta and construction of the newly named State Water Project. Carley Porter, who had steered the Burns-Porter Act through the Assembly two years before, spearheaded the defensive action and all of the amendments were voted down. It had been 11 years since A.D. Edmonston originally proposed the State Water Project. Now California was finally ready to build the world's largest water system.

Chapter 10

BUILDING A WATER LIFELINE

In California, the decade from 1962 through 1972 echoed with the mighty sounds of an orchestra of heavy equipment as workers and machines toiled to build the largest water development project in history. The State Water Project was awesome in scale, extending more than 600 miles from remote dams in the alpine wilderness of the Sierra Nevada range to the arid chaparral surrounding Lake Perris in distant Riverside County.

In 1964 the U.S. Supreme Court issued its decree in the long-contested case of *Arizona vs. California.*

At the same time, local water agencies throughout the state engaged in formidable efforts to build facilities that would transport water from the state's new lifeline to homes, industry and farmers' fields. And it would be sorely needed, for California's population had soared past the 17.3 million mark by the time project contruction *started* in 1962. Californians outnumbered New Yorkers, making the Golden State the most populous state in the nation, and there seemed no end to the influx of newcomers.

The population explosion was greatest in Southern California where Metropolitan began an expansion program that was almost as costly as the state project itself. To deliver Northern California water to its member agencies, Metropolitan had to build more than 300 miles of major pipelines and tunnels. Many of these were to be routed under busy city and suburban streets. It was a massive and complicated undertaking with a price tag to match — $1.3 billion.

The State Water Project and the expansion assumed even greater importance to the Southland when in 1964 the U.S. Supreme Court issued its decree in the long-contested case of *Arizona vs. California* which determined entitlements of the use of Colorado River water. Essentially a victory for Arizona, Metropolitan was the ultimate odd-man-out in the Colorado River numbers game that had stretched over decades. With water rights junior to those of three California agricultural agencies with claims on the river, the district would eventually lose more than 662,000 acre-feet of water each year, well over half the 1.2 million acre-feet for which it had contract rights. In time, much of this shortfall would be expected to come from the State Water Project.

Construction of bridge over the Middle Fork of the Feather River begins in 1964.

But first, the complex, gigantic state system had to be built. Designed to ultimately deliver 4.23 million acre-feet of water, year in and year out, regardless of weather conditions, the project also would provide flood control, hydroelectric power and recreation. In addition, it had to benefit fisheries and wildlife habitat. To accomplish this, state plans called for 23 dams and reservoirs, 22 pumping plants, six power plants, 473 miles of canals, 175 miles of pipelines and 20 miles of tunnels.

The first major facility and cornerstone of the State Water Project was Oroville Dam on the Feather River. With a capacity of more than 3.5 million acre-feet, water stored in Lake Oroville behind the dam would be released to generate power and flow down the Feather River into the Sacramento, through which it would course into the Sacramento-San Joaquin Delta. Water then would be pumped out of the southern delta close to the town of Tracy into the 444-mile California Aqueduct. The Burns-Porter Act specified that appropriate facilities be built to transport water more efficiently across the delta than the natural channels of the region. Moreover, these facilities would have the added purpose of protecting the delta environment. The North and South Bay Aqueducts would branch off to serve areas above and below San Francisco. The city by the Golden Gate itself had rejected the opportunity of becoming a contractor for state project water.

Continuing on a southern course, California Aqueduct water would flow 73 miles south of the delta to San Luis Reservoir, the second major storage facility of the system. Capable of storing more than 2 million acre-feet of water, San Luis was designed to be jointly owned and operated by the state and federal governments. From there, water would continue down the western side of the San Joaquin Valley, the aqueduct being a joint-use project with the federal government as far as Kettleman City. A Coastal

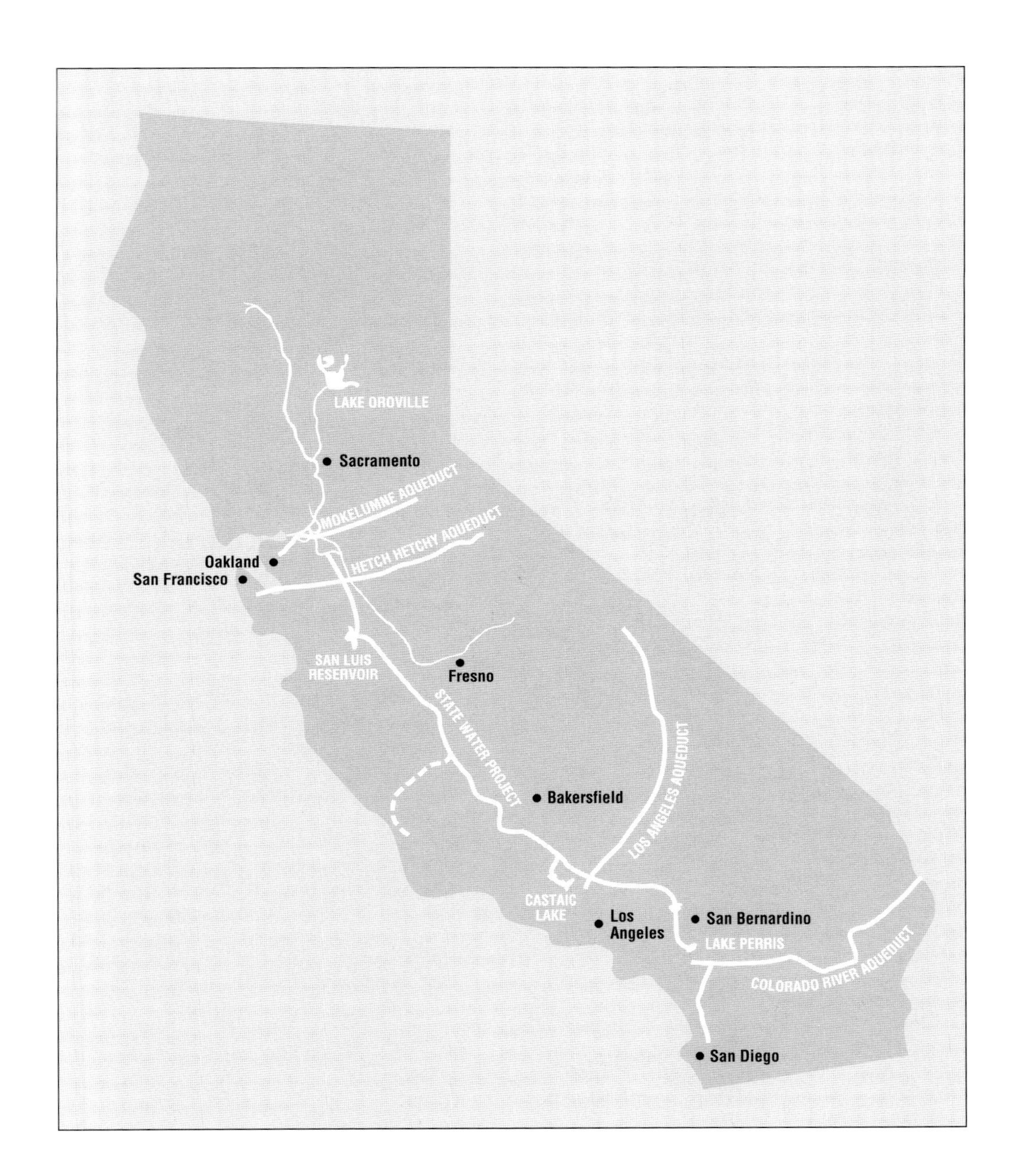

Branch would angle off to the southwest to serve San Luis Obispo and Santa Barbara counties. At the southern end of the valley, water would have to "leapfrog" almost 2,000 feet over the Tehachapi Mountains. At this point, the aqueduct would separate into east and west branches — the West Branch transporting water to Castaic Lake, north of the San Fernando Valley, and the East Branch skirting the Los Angeles basin and extending another 140 miles before terminating at Lake Perris near Riverside.

William Warne

Actually building a water system on this scale was an immensely complicated proposition, so when Harvey Banks, director of the Department of Water Resources, retired, Governor Brown knew he needed a leader with bulldog determination to replace him. The man he selected was William Warne, a veteran administrator with a get-things-done-no-matter-how-difficult-the-challenge reputation. Before assuming the DWR directorship, he had headed the departments of Agriculture and Fish and Game under Brown. He also had worked for the Bureau of Reclamation and had been an assistant secretary of the US Department of the Interior.

Warne and an expanded team of DWR engineers, hired to translate A.D. Edmonston's plan from paper to concrete, faced four arduous, unique engineering challenges. Over the next decade, they would find ingenious ways to build Oroville Dam and its huge underground powerhouse; stabilize the powdery, dry earth of the southern San Joaquin Valley; and propel a river of water up and over a mountain range. And these things were done. A solution was found for the fourth problem, as well: a method for improving water flows across the Sacramento-San Joaquin Delta while also providing protection for that environmentally sensitive region. But it was never implemented. Rather, the delta and the proposed solution — the Peripheral Canal — became political "hot potatoes" in a controversy that has endured for nearly three decades.

Warne's approach to building the State Water Project was pragmatic and direct. "My philosophy always has been to build facilities as quickly as you can to keep the costs down," he said. That's what DWR tried to accomplish. Construction was planned in stages, allowing water to be delivered to contractors as soon as possible. Later some facilities would be expanded and others would be added to the system allowing the state to meet the full entitlements of its customers. From the start of construction, the State

Water Project was thought of as the first phase of the much larger and more encompassing California Water Plan which had been issued in 1957.

To build the system within Warne's timetable, the project's first engineering hurdle, Oroville Dam, had to be tackled at the outset. Without Oroville, there would no aqueduct system because the dam was designed to collect and hold water to be used by the project contractors. By the start of construction in the summer of 1962, a massive amount of preliminary work had been completed and the type of dam selected. Comprehensive geological studies had been made of the dam site and advice on what type of dam to construct sought from leading engineers around the world. After considering all kinds of designs — including one striking concrete arch dam advocated by a French designer — it had been decided to build an earthfill dam. But this was to be no prosaic earthen dam; it was to be the world's biggest, with the structure rising 770 feet from the bedrock underlying the Feather River.

Much of the material used in building Oroville Dam was a legacy from another age. Immense heaps of dredger tailings left along the riverbanks of the Mother Lode country decades earlier by hydraulic miners would supply the material. A consortium of seven construction companies, operating under the name of Oroville Constructors, won the civil engineering contract to move the mountains of tailings and build the dam. An estimated 168 million tons of earthen fill would be required; to move the tailings, an innovative transportation system was devised to traverse the 12 miles to the dam site, utilizing a system that included a railroad, conveyor belts, a fleet of trucks and a machine called a bucket-wheel excavator. The latter was adapted from strip mining and had a passing resemblance to a carnival ferris wheel. The machine contained a 30-foot-diameter wheel that turned and twisted so its eight giant, bucket-like appendages could chew up the tailings, carry off huge bites and spill them onto a conveyor belt.

WARNE'S APPROACH TO BUILDING THE STATE WATER PROJECT WAS PRAGMATIC AND DIRECT.

The conveyor transported the tailings to a loading area where they were

Moving the dredger tailings to the dam site: a round-the-clock operation

piled onto gondola cars of the Oroville railroad. Four sets of 40 gondola cars and eight 2,500-horsepower locomotives, the most powerful in the world, operating in pairs, carried the loads to their destination. The Oroville line performed on a timetable that rivaled the punctuality of German railroads. All four trains were in constant use. When a train arrived at the dam site, the specially designed gondola cars were emptied in pairs. The cars, constructed with rotating couplings allowing them to be flipped over, dumped their loads onto a second conveyor belt. It ferried the tailings over the Feather River to a yard where they were sorted and stockpiled. As they were needed, the materials were carried by another conveyor up the face of the slowly growing dam to be loaded onto trucks. The vehicles finished the job by carrying the sorted tailings to where they were required on the dam.

"They [the crews] worked like this around the clock in three shifts, at first on a six-day schedule with the seventh for maintenance; later, on a seven-day schedule," said Howard Eastin, who worked for DWR as an engineer at Oroville. "The whole system worked very well and the contractors were proud they were moving more tons of material per day than any other railroad in the country."

Eastin also was involved in the second half of the engineering challenge at Oroville. Excavating the 550-foot-long subterranean powerhouse hidden beneath the left abutment of Oroville Dam proved a Herculean task as access was extremely restricted. In fact, there was only one point through which all the materials and equipment could be funneled in and out. Again, tight scheduling became a critical factor in meeting completion dates as engineers directed a tricky operation using new construction methods.

"The excavation had to be done extremely carefully so it would not collapse," explained Eastin. "We were using state-of-the-art design and techniques on the roof which would not be reinforced with concrete. Instead, we used rock bolts, some up to 40 feet long. They were drilled into the rock and tension held the rock together. Very few contractors had seen anything like the bolts, and we had to educate them and the unions to assure everyone the project could be safely constructed."

Once the dual Oroville tasks were under control, problem-solving efforts shifted to the San Joaquin Valley where an entirely different sort of challenge existed. Warne explained, "You can't build a wavy canal, one that dips up and down. But that's what the state would have wound up with if the California Aqueduct had been built without doing something to consolidate the unsettled soil over long stretches in the southern San Joaquin Valley."

Curiously, water proved both the cause and solution. The fertile loess — soil deposited on the valley floor over the course of thousands of years — had the unfortunate habit of settling and collapsing when water was applied, as the ground had never been saturated in that dry climate. To prevent the

Giant settling ponds to compact soil stretched mile after mile along the route of the planned project.

aqueduct from sinking when the land subsided, it was decided to flood a huge swath of land more than 50 miles long on the project route. Hundreds of giant ponds were created along the way and countless infiltration wells sunk to soak the dry earth. In some places, the soil greedily drank up the water and compacted quickly; in others, it took more than a year for the water to soak in and settle. The subsidence in some locations was as great as nine feet, but the liberal application of water had firmed up the land to expedite construction of the aqueduct.

The third challenge — and perhaps the most severe from an engineering standpoint — was met at the extreme southern tip of the San Joaquin Valley, where the Tehachapi Mountains rise. A range noteworthy more for its jumbled geological composition than its height, it is one of the comparatively few major mountain ranges in the United States that has an east-west rather than north-south orientation. The Tehachapis were bisected by earthquake faults, including the state's notorious San Andreas. Yet, there was no avoiding this major fault. The aqueduct had to pass near and eventually cross it, as would any pipeline from the north bringing water into Southern California. Planning was complicated by another fault — the Garlock, at the crest of the mountains. Although the Garlock is considered inactive, it too would have to be crossed. Earthquake safety was a prime concern from the inception of the project, and for this reason, proposals to tunnel through the Tehachapis, rather than building over them, were rejected early on.

"It was the most spectacular engineering problem of the entire project," declared Warne. "Here we were planning to lift the largest amount of water over the highest distance in history in the immediate vicinity of two earthquake faults. We were determined not to cross a fault in a tunnel. We wanted to build a facility that could be repaired quickly if it was damaged by an earthquake."

Having determined not to tunnel through the stubborn Tehachapis, the

Unimpressive exterior of A.D. Edmonston pumping plant at the base of the Tehachapis belies its "big-lift" purpose.

state would have to pump water some 2,000 feet over them — which was exactly what A.D. Edmonston had envisioned in 1950 when he sketched out the State Water Project. Determining the safest and most efficient way to boost the water over the top became the subject of intense debate and study. Metropolitan and DWR had different ideas about achieving this

The Southland's water-supply bucket suddenly had sprung a major leak.

goal. Metropolitan favored pumping the water over the Tehachapis in stages by utilizing a series of two or three pumping plants and small storage reservoirs. Conversely, the state wanted to "climb the mountains" in one giant lift of some 2,100 feet. To resolve this issue, consultants from around the world were employed to analyze the unique conditions of the Tehachapis. For a year, a variety of pumps and designs were tested at the National Engineering Laboratory in East Kilbride, Scotland. Ultimately, DWR's single-lift proposal proved to be the best option and was selected in 1966. The exhaustive studies paid off, resulting in the world's most advanced pumps and a slight alteration in the aqueduct route, dropping the required pump lift by nearly 200 feet, down to 1,926.

While Warne was spurring the construction of the State Water Project, Metropolitan was equally busy. As a result of the Supreme Court decision in *Arizona vs. California,* the Southland's water-supply bucket suddenly had sprung a major leak. Well over half the water for which Metropolitan had contracted with the federal government more than a generation before, in effect, had been awarded to Arizona. As a result of the court decision, California was limited to using 4.4 million acre-feet of water a year from the Colorado River. At the time the Supreme Court decree was issued, California, under federal contracts, was using about 5 million acre-feet annually. It would have to begin restricting its use of Colorado River water once Arizona started using its full entitlement of 2.8 million acre-feet. Although construction of the Central Arizona Project would postpone that eventuality until the early 1990s, Metropolitan immediately began searching for an alternate water source.

Metropolitan looked northward because the State Water Project was the logical place to seek replacement water. Construction was still in the early stages and, more importantly, all of the estimated 4.23 million-acre-foot annual yield hadn't yet been subscribed. So in 1964, the state permitted Metropolitan to increase its ultimate entitlement by 500,000 acre-feet to

2,011,500 acre-feet. The state also allowed other contractors to boost their allotments by 15 percent.

Meanwhile, Metropolitan was moving ahead on its expansion program. Proposition W, an $850 million general obligation bond issue was passed by voters in 1966 to launch construction. It was a massive undertaking, because Metropolitan was installing giant pipelines — some with a diameter of 17 feet, the largest concrete pipe ever manufactured — to handle the water from Northern California. While a number of these water lines, or feeders, traversed undeveloped areas, others cut through the heart of the congested metropolis. None was more tricky to build than the Sepulveda Feeder which extended 45 miles from Granada Hills to the Palos Verdes Peninsula.

System expansion was disruptive.

"It was a nightmare," recalled Evan Griffith, who was chief construction engineer during the expansion effort and later became Metropolitan's general manager. "Traffic had to be rerouted, there were only a couple of lanes open on Sepulveda Boulevard and people were really screaming." Frank Clinton, another former Metropolitan general manager who was the chief project engineer for the expansion, added, "Our big problem was finding streets that hadn't already been filled by all kinds of buried utilities — gas lines, water mains, telephone cables. And we had to find streets in which we could put eight-foot-diameter pipe."

Two tragedies marred the expansion effort. In February 1971, the killer Sylmar earthquake rumbled through Southern California, doing extensive damage in the San Fernando Valley, wreaking havoc on the new Jensen filtration plant there that was nearing completion. It would take close to a year to repair the damages. Four months later, a deadly accident occurred involving a tunnel machine that was being used by a firm under contract to Metropolitan to dig the San Fernando Tunnel for the Foothill Feeder project. A nighttime gas explosion claimed several lives.

Freighter makes its way toward ocean in delta ship channel.

While Metropolitan was pressing ahead with its expansion, the state continued its construction effort. Slowly, the State Water Project turned from a blueprint dream into reality — with the exception of a facility to cross the Sacramento-San Joaquin Delta. A vaguely triangular-shaped mass of nearly three-quarters of a million acres, the delta is the hub of California's water resources, and any statewide water system would have to take it into consideration. From the initial planning stages of the State Water Project, the dual challenges of moving surplus water across the delta for export and protecting the environment while helping correct existing natural and man-made problems were recognized. The delta in its existing configuration wouldn't work because its channels lacked the capacity to carry sufficient water. And though the Burns-Porter Act had been carefully worded, the section describing delta facilities deliberately had been left hazy.

"I remember a meeting in Harvey Banks' office when the legislation was being drafted," recalled Walter Schultz, then a DWR engineer. "When it came to the delta, they didn't want to be too specific and close the door on moving things around. Ralph Brody came up with the key phrase, 'facilities for transfer of water across the delta,' and those words were used in the Burns-Porter Act."

The Brown administration couldn't be faulted for adopting that tack because in 1959 no delta solution had been identified that didn't create more problems than it proposed to solve. Up to that time most of the proposals for crossing the delta involved building some type of barrier in San Francisco Bay or along the delta's western rim to prevent saltwater intrusion. A number of these plans, first advanced as early as the 1920s, though grandiose in scale, were, nevertheless, seriously considered. But barriers were not a practical solution. An alternative proposal, the Waterway Control Plan, emerged later in 1959. It suggested using a number of existing delta channels to carry water for local use as well as moving water to the south delta where it could be exported. In addition, a number of channels would be blocked to redirect water flows to regions of the delta where freshwater was needed. Though the plan did suggest a new approach, it proved impossible to sell.

Merging delta channels

"It cut off some waterways, changed tidal flows and caused fish and wildlife problems," explained Langdon Owen, a DWR engineer given the assignment of selling the Waterway Control Plan to the public. "Yachting clubs, the Department of Fish and Game and even garden clubs opposed it. It wasn't politically possible to build it, and a lot of arguments used against the plan were right. People were claiming environmental damage before the days of the environmentalists."

Owen recommended an ecological study of the delta, which in turn led to the formation of the Interagency Delta Committee. Made up of local, state and federal agencies, this group studied various barrier and waterway proposals until the kernel of a new idea began to form in 1962.

Warne authorized construction of the Peripheral Canal in March of 1966.

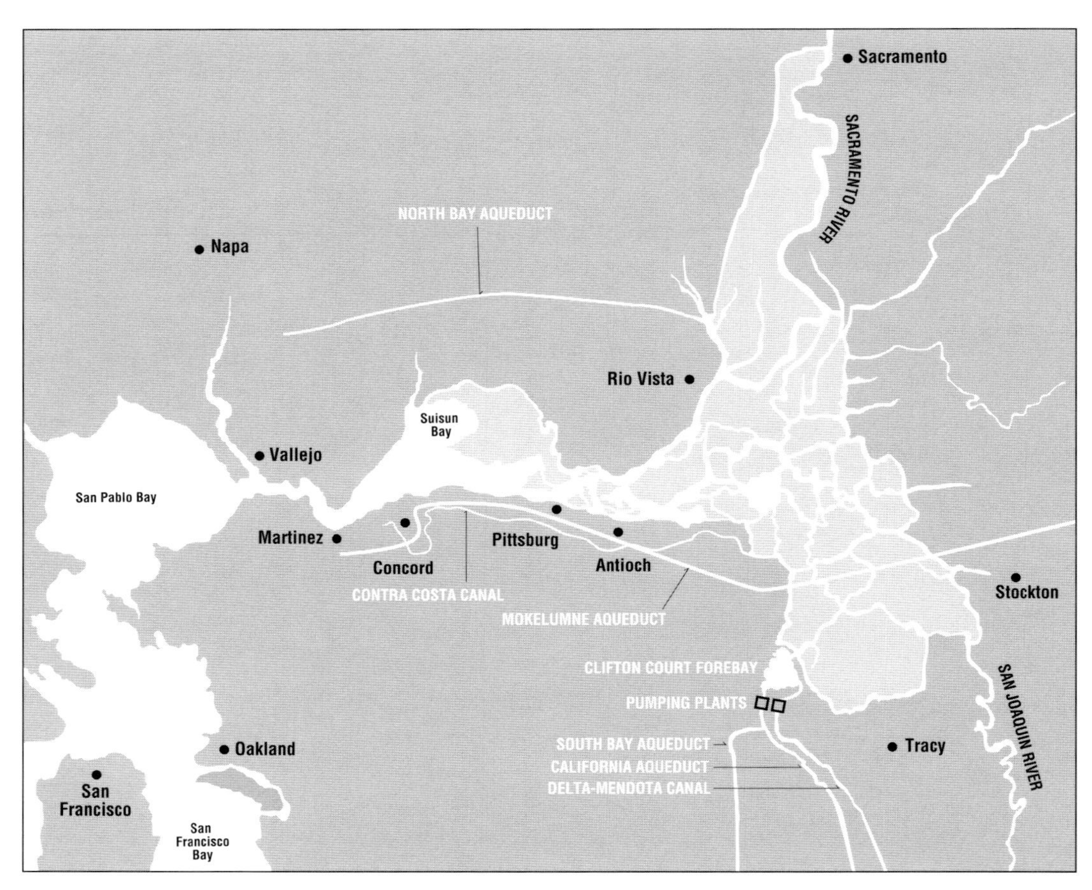

The Sacramento-San Joaquin Delta

"We became aware that the solution wasn't in the existing delta channels," Owen elaborated. "With each plan, we slowly moved further and further away from that concept, until we finally looked toward the delta's periphery or edge and came up with the Peripheral Canal."

The Peripheral Canal option began to dominate as it and other delta solutions were reviewed. The Peripheral Canal, proposed at that time and little altered since, was a 42-mile, unlined channel that would skirt the delta's eastern edge. Designed to carry water to the southern delta near the town of Tracy, where SWP pumps would draw it off, the canal was independent of existing waterways. However, it would release water into delta channels at 14 key points along the way. These freshwater releases would block saltwater from entering the delta and eliminate the reverse flows of water being created by SWP and CVP pumps to the south. Other important benefits of the Peripheral Canal included much improved water quality, both for export and for local users, fish and wildlife habitat enhancement, and seismic safety.

The state decided to go ahead with the Peripheral Canal in March of 1966, and Warne authorized its construction as the delta-transfer facility specified in the Burns-Porter Act. Work was scheduled to begin in 1967, and the state began buying up land. But the water project ground to a halt when Ronald Reagan began his first term as governor in January 1969.

The project was faced with a cash flow problem because deliveries to contractors were still minimal. Thus, Reagan and his DWR director William Gianelli concentrated their state project efforts on developing new revenue sources to maintain the pace of construction. The inflated economy had forced the state to raise the interest rate on its water project bonds. Gianelli was able to give the project about a $400 million boost by using a provision in the Burns-Porter Act that allowed the state to sell revenue bonds. Such authority originally had been granted for the Central Valley Project in the depression days of the 1930s when it was near impossible to sell bonds. Gianelli used the funds from the sale of revenue bonds, additional funds from the tidelands oil revenues and a stretched-out construction schedule to keep the project moving. Among the facilities deferred for later construction was the Peripheral Canal.

Artist's conception of the Peripheral Canal

Gianelli and Reagan had felt other facilities should be built first so some water could be delivered to contractors throughout the state. Alameda County and Santa Clara Valley water districts in Northern California had been the first contractors to take deliveries back in 1962 and 1965 through temporary connections. These were replaced in 1969 when the South Bay Aqueduct was completed. In 1968, water began rushing down the California Aqueduct into Kern County. In Southern California, the long-awaited water from the Feather River finally completed its journey over the Tehachapis and into the West Branch of the California Aqueduct, reaching Castaic Lake, the terminal reservoir, in April 1972. Work on the East Branch was finished 13 months later, with delivery of water to its terminal reservoir, Lake Perris.

Throughout the remaining two years of the Reagan era, efforts to commence construction of the Peripheral Canal proceeded fitfully. In 1973, a decade-long study of delta problems was completed by the Department of Fish and Game — endorsing the Peripheral Canal. Several months later, Gianelli approved the partial excavation of 10 miles along the canal's route to provide road fill for the construction of Interstate Highway 5 nearby. That was as close as the Reagan administration would get to building the transdelta facility.

"We were still planning to build the canal," said Gianelli, who retired a short time later. "We had the legal authority to do it, but I continued to defer it because I was convinced that it wasn't needed yet." Shortly after Gianelli's retirement, the Department of Water Resources issued a draft Environmental Impact Report on the canal. It became a lightning rod,

"Looking back, if there were mistakes made on the state project, the outstanding one was delaying the Peripheral Canal."
—*Teerink*

attracting the ire of environmentalists. The canal was in the final stages of engineering design at that point, and John Teerink, the new DWR director, hesitated in awarding the first construction contract.

"Looking back, if there were mistakes made on the state project, the outstanding one was delaying the Peripheral Canal," said Teerink, who had helped A. D. Edmonston plan the system 20 years before. "We didn't know then the roadblocks we'd face, and the Peripheral Canal looked like an item that could be deferred. It was really a question of when do you put it on line rather than anything else."

In the course of a single decade, California had built the skeleton of its water lifeline, one that could serve all of its contracting agencies. But it was far from having the ability to fulfill contracts for 4.23 million acre-feet a year without creating more storage capacity and a delta transfer facility. How California would keep its commitment to complete its monumental task would be passed along to a new generation of leaders. Any decision would have to involve tackling the complex problems of the Sacramento-San Joaquin Delta.

Governor Ronald Reagan at the groundbreaking for Perris Dam and Reservoir

THE DELTA IS A FRAGILE ENTITY, FACED ON ALL SIDES BY A MULTITUDE OF COMPETING INTERESTS.

Casting the delta

Chapter 11

THE DELTA QUANDARY

The Sacramento-San Joaquin Delta. The state depends on it for 40 percent of its drinking water and almost half of its agricultural water. Yet it is a fragile dependency because the delta itself is a fragile entity. Faced on all sides by a multitude of competing interests, it has become all things to all people.

Its waters irrigate and drain millions of acres of farmland, repel ceaseless incoming saltwater tides from San Francisco Bay, nurture a rich fishery, aid in manufacturing a broad variety of products ranging from cardboard to chemicals, provide a highway for cargo ships, furnish drinking water to the overwhelming majority of Californians, harbor a sanctuary for wildlife and endow the state with an expansive recreational playground. Each of these is a beneficial use; some are in conflict with others.

For the past quarter of a century, Californians have debated the future of the delta. Questions concerning its environment and preserving its water quality have been central to often bitter debates; and somewhere in these cacophonous exchanges, one essential fact most often goes overlooked. Above all, the modern delta has been shaped by man and is vastly different than when first glimpsed by Europeans who looked, as Keats might well have characterized the feeling, with "wild surmise" upon its natural state.

While Native Americans hunted in the Sacramento-San Joaquin Delta as long as 4,000 years ago, the first recorded description of the region is little more than 200 years old. Spanish soldiers, under the command of Captain Pedro Fages, exploring eastward from San Francisco in 1772 in search of new mission sites, found their way obstructed. Fages found "a sea of reeds" extending to the horizon, so inpenetrable it discouraged further exploration. The Spanish made only two more probes of the area by sea in 1775 and 1776 before losing interest: during one, Don Juan Ayala captained the San Carlos up San Francisco Bay to a point west of Chipps Island, today considered to be the entryway to the delta.

One day, miners; the next, farmers and levee builders

Fages and Ayala looked upon a landscape that was perhaps 11,000 years in the making. It was born at the end of the last Ice Age when sea levels rose around the world, flooding shallow areas such as the delta. The region became one vast marsh of about 750,000 acres watered by the incoming ocean tides and the runoff from innumerable mountain streams. Then, as now, the overwhelming majority of freshwater was provided by the Sacramento River which, along with its tributaries, drains the northern Sierra Nevada, Coast and Cascade ranges. From the east and south, Dry Creek and the Calaveras, Consumnes, Mokelumne and San Joaquin rivers, along with tributaries of the San Joaquin including the Stanislaus, the Tuolumne, the Merced, the Chowchilla and the Fresno, contributed lesser but still significant amounts of water. Marsh grasses and reeds eventually took root in the thin soil deposited by these rivers. For thousands of years they flourished, only to be buried under flooding waters, covered with silt and then flourish again. Layer upon layer of this organic material accumulated and was gradually transformed into the peat soils of the delta. The soil was incredibly fertile, but disguised under its mantle of water and reeds.

Gold was the indirect agent of change in the delta, as it was for so many locales in California. San Francisco Bay, the delta and the rivers feeding it offered the easiest and most direct route to the Mother Lode country for thousands of gold-crazed fortune hunters. But prospecting, with its adversity and hardship, wasn't for everyone. Miners began drifting back out of the foothills. Some who had sown the soil elsewhere discovered the rich peat underlying the delta and began farming. This touched off an eighty-year effort to claim the region for agriculture.

The transformation of the delta began in the 1850s, initially by hand with the sweat of cheap labor provided mostly by Chinese workmen. Settlers and coolies hacked blocks of peat from high spots with tule knives and then piled them atop each other to form levees to hold back the waters. Miles and miles of levees were raised and the land was left to dry out.

Later, emboldened by the success hydraulic miners had in tearing down the hillsides of the Sierra Nevada with their technology, Californians turned to machines to build more miles of levees to create delta islands. This time the earth-forming was achieved with dredges. Starting in 1863, existing delta waterways were deepened and pushed in different directions as the dredges sucked vast amounts of channel debris and peat in what has become the never-ending job of levee building and repair.

By the time this massive reclamation effort was completed in 1930, the landscape of the delta had been thoroughly altered. More than half a million acres had been enveloped by 1,100 miles of levees. Fages' sea of reeds had been changed into an inland archipelago of some 70 islands encircled by more than 700 miles of rivers, sloughs and channels. Much of this land has been devoted to farming and has produced generous amounts of corn, the delta's most important crop, along with safflower, sugar beets, alfalfa, vegetables, wheat, grapes, pears, walnuts and other crops.

Dredge Thor is at work near Stockton as 1893 pleasure seekers paddle by.

But delta farming is a precarious enterprise, sowing the seeds of its own destruction. As much as 150,000 acres of the cultivated land in the delta are below sea level. Relentlessly, the saltwater of San Francisco Bay seeks an opportunity to rush in from the west, as it has done in dry periods historically. Only freshwater entering the delta and miles of levees can halt this constant saline encroachment. However, time is on the side of the incoming seaborne tides because of the intrinsic weakness of the peat backbone of the delta.

A poor building material, peat is the basis of modern delta levees, which along with the farmland, are slowly sinking. The very act of heaping up piles of peat to create levees caused problems. The weight of the levee pushes down on the unstable soil beneath, causing the levee to subside. As more soil is added on top, the process continues. Meanwhile, the levees are being attacked in other ways. Peat is porous and absorbs copious amounts of water, therefore softening them. The material crumbles easily and the wave action in delta channels readily erodes and undercuts levee banks. Burrowing animals are another concern; more than once, sections of levees have collapsed after an animal dug a tiny tunnel that then was widened by inrushing water. Portions of delta farmland are steadily sinking at the rate of two to three inches every year. Problems are compounded by heavy farming equipment which compacts the pliant soil. And, finally, digging up peat for cultivation allows the soil to dry out, oxidize and then, in its lightweight state, become a victim of wind erosion, simply blowing away.

THE PROBLEM OF DELTA WATER QUALITY IS AS CONVOLUTED AS SOME OF THE CHANNELS THAT MEANDER THROUGH THE REGION.

Subsidence has been occurring for decades, leaving such small delta towns as Isleton and the Chinese-founded community of Locke entirely below sea level. Of the delta's 70 islands, close to 50 sit a minimum of two feet below. Only the fragile levees protect these islands and their towns from flooding, and levees have failed well over 100 times in the 20th century.

The problem of delta water quality is as convoluted as some of the channels that meander through the region. That quality is largely, but not totally, the result of the daily tug of war between the freshwater in the delta and the incoming tidal surges of saltwater. Because the delta's waterways lie at sea level, saltwater constantly seeks entrance into its channels; at the same time, freshwater pours into the delta from the Sacramento and other rivers, repelling the incoming tide. At times, there is not enough freshwater available and saltwater intrudes into the western delta and beyond. Before such dams as Oroville and Shasta were built to control winter flooding and provide summer releases of water, saltwater intrusion in the delta was a persistent problem. In fact, in the first three decades of the 20th century, saltwater at different times reached all the way to Sacramento and Stockton.

Saltwater intrusion is a fact of life in the delta because the flows of freshwater are highly variable. Those flows change from season to season and from year to year as a result of the rainfall and snowpack in the watersheds

Another fragile levee succumbs.

upstream of the delta. Moreover, powerful Pacific storms can pelt the state in the winter, propelling as much as 2 million acre-feet of flood waters through the delta in that time period. The Department of Water Resources has charted some striking variations in annual flows. In 1969, a wet year, 43.3 million acre-feet of freshwater poured into the delta. Just eight years later, in 1977, less than a seventh of that, just 5.9 million acre-feet trickled into the delta during the second and last year of a severe drought. A long-term study of delta water resources, covering 1922 to 1954, marked the annual delta inflow at 19.8 million acre-feet, considerably more water than the Colorado River carries each year.

In the natural scheme of things, more water would be available in the winter during the rainy season and spring when snowmelt pours off the mountains, and, conversely, less in the dry summer and autumn. But the delta no longer is a natural system. It has been altered by water resources development, both within and outside its boundaries. Local, state and federal agencies have built 42 dams to collect and store water on rivers feeding the delta and their tributaries. These dams provide vital flood control facilities, allow water to be stored so the seasonal flows into the delta can be equalized and provide water for export.

Such exports have benefitted both urban and agricultural areas statewide. Though California has been drawing water directly from the delta for export only since 1940, indirect exports began earlier with the completion in 1929 of the East Bay Municipal Utility District's Mokelumne Aqueduct. By damming and tapping into the Mokelumne River, East Bay MUD was siphoning water that would have spilled into the delta. Five years later this process was duplicated on the Tuolumne River when San Francisco finished its Hetch Hetchy Aqueduct, a project for which the sale of bonds had been approved by the voters of the city by the bay in 1910. Direct delta export began with the completion in 1940 of the Contra Costa Canal, the initial unit of the federal government's Central Valley Project. Then in 1951, the CVP's Tracy Pumping Plant also began taking water out of the south delta for the San Joaquin Valley, and in 1968 the State Water Project's delta pumping plant went into operation in the same area.

Pumping in the south delta complicates the water quality situation. Existing delta channels — carved by nature, lined with levees by man — do not have adequate capacity to carry freshwater to all parts of the delta. Export pumps are powerful enough to create reverse flows in some channels, at times drawing brackish water into the delta interior, replacing the freshwater that is being exported. In addition to degrading water quality, the reverse flows also have a negative effect on migrating fish which become confused as they attempt to traverse delta waterways.

Two more elements must be considered to complete the delta water quality equation — agricultural wastes and the possibility of levee failures. Agricultural wastes end up in the water in three primary ways: they filter out of irrigated farmland into streams which carry them into the delta;

A delta pump siphons water for agricultural use.

Indirect delta exports began with East Bay MUD's Mokelumne Aqueduct and the process was duplicated with San Francisco's Hetch Hetchy system. Direct delta export began with the Contra Costa Canal.

Agricultural runoff flows into the delta.

they are transported by drains which empty directly into the estuary; and they enter the waters from local farming activity. The precarious stability of delta levees is like a time bomb to delta water quality. Ambitious state and federal programs costing hundreds of millions of dollars repeatedly have been proposed to prop up and rehabilitate hundreds of miles of levees. If something comprehensive isn't done soon, they inevitably will fail, saltwater will rush in to fill the exposed islands and water quality will be the victim.

Almost from the time Californians first began tinkering with the delta, plans have been proposed for curing its problems. As far back as 1860, there was discussion of erecting barriers that would prevent saltwater from entering, transforming the delta into a freshwater lake. The most sweeping barrier proposition conceived was the Reber Plan of the late 1940s which called for constructing a series of giant barriers across San Francisco Bay. The brainchild of one-time actor and drama teacher John Reber, the plan would have converted both bay and delta into one expansive freshwater reservoir. Reber promoted his plan with the zeal of a missionary and, at one point, had the support of several federal agencies. His proposal was creative and well-engineered, but in the early 1950s, it began to unravel under close examination. The huge reservoir he envisioned would actually have lost more water through evaporation than it would have saved and the barriers would have proved an ecological disaster. Yet, elements of the Reber Plan have reappeared over the years in the constant search for a delta solution.

In the late 1950s, the state hired Dutch engineer Cornelius Biemond as a consultant to examine flood control problems. Biemond, who had been involved in Holland's epic efforts to reclaim farmland in the Zuider Zee from the North Sea, advocated a major physical reshaping of the delta. He didn't think it was economically possible to protect all of the existing islands from flooding and suggested consolidating them into four or five very large islands. Calling for blocking many channels and building new ones to improve water quality and to divert water to the south delta for exportation, Biemond's plan was doomed by its high cost and voices raised in opposition to blocking delta channels. But like the Reber Plan, certain elements of Biemond's work live on in new proposals that would change delta water flows either by building new cross-delta channels or blocking others.

More recently, efforts to solve delta problems have centered on operating regulations and procedures. Local, state and federal agencies which take water from the delta today function under a set of 1978 standards established by the State Water Resources Control Board in its Decision 1485, or D-1485 for short. These standards were designed to protect the three basic beneficial uses in the delta — municipal and industrial, agricultural, and fish and wildlife. The State Water Resources Control Board determined to review water quality standards for the delta and San Francisco Bay every 10 years. But as a practical matter, this review is evolving into a continuous process. Delta water quality and operations are too important to be considered

THE PLAN WOULD HAVE CONVERTED BOTH BAY AND DELTA INTO ONE EXPANSIVE FRESHWATER RESERVOIR.

Well-traveled dike separates the Netherlands' Lake Ijssel (formerly the Zuider Zee) from the North Sea.

Mending a levee break

only once a decade, particularly in light of more stringent state and federal health regulations governing household water quality. In fact, the latest round of bay-delta hearings has been under way since July of 1987 and, like most things concerning the delta, has provoked heated controversy.

A draft plan released late in 1988, after drawing broad-based criticism, was withdrawn; a subsequent plan is the subject of criticism by the Environmental Protection Agency; and the State Water Resources Control Board continues to wrestle with the process of establishing new standards for the 1990s. These standards are vital to the health and protection of the delta and they must balance the beneficial but sometimes competing uses of water.

Throughout the state, there is little argument about two things: the delta has to be protected and it has problems. Many view the Sacramento-San Joaquin Delta of the late 20th century, shaped and molded by a myriad of human hands, as a very inefficient system for transferring water. California has no choice but to repair the damages caused by past activities. It does have a choice, however, as to how. It is a decision that can't be postponed indefinitely, for too many people, too much of California's wildlife resources, too many businesses and too much industry rely on the delta for water.

Chapter 12

THE CANAL THAT WASN'T

California came into its own in the decades of the 1970s and '80s. Increasingly, the state blossomed into a national leadership role, creating and setting trends in culture, finance and business, and even in politics. It played a major role as the United States increased its economic focus on Asia and the expanding trade and business ventures in the Pacific Rim. The state's thriving economy grew even more robust, outstripping all but a handful of nations. Culturally, California built on its long-established reputation as the movie capitol of the world, taking the lead in the nation in building museums, art galleries and performance centers for music, opera and dance, while remaining on the cutting edge in architecture, fashion and lifestyle. And, indeed, the state firmed its grasp on the national political reins, seeing two of its "favorite sons," Richard Nixon and Ronald Reagan, occupying the White House.

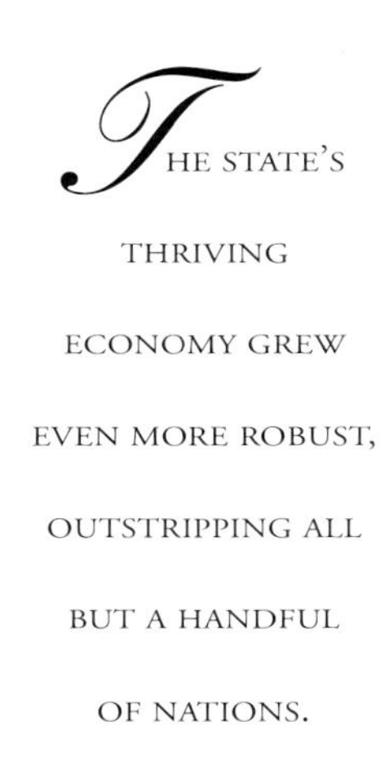

During these two decades, California continued as a social magnet of sorts, attracting new residents as the fulcrum of U.S. population swung

1970: The Southland population continues to grow — and downtown Los Angeles along with it.

Planning for their future was becoming less certain in 1970...

...a growing concern in 1975

...and blocked at every turn by 1980.

dramatically from the Northeast to the South and the West. As the 1990s dawned, the state boasted almost 30 million people, a cool 10 million increase over 1970. Most of this population explosion took place in the 1980s with the addition of 6 million. According to the Center for Continuing Study of the California Economy, a private Palo Alto firm, this proliferation constituted the greatest growth any state had ever made in a single decade. There are more Californians today than there are Canadians, Czechoslovakians, Iraqis, North Koreans or Australians. In fact, only 28 nations have more residents than California. Further, the center projects that the Golden State's population will continue to expand twice as fast as the rest of the country, increasing by another 10 million residents by 2010.

At the same time California was expanding its leadership role and experiencing this phenomenal crush of new citizens, a curious thing happened. After more than 70 years of vigorously developing the state's natural resources, California put on the brakes. Work on augmenting the most critical and elemental of these resources, the state's water supply, came to a screeching halt — the issue of water was thrust more than ever into the political arena. North-south rivalry became more divisive and strident as Northern Californians lined up against water development and diligently fought to protect perceived threats to "their" water, the delta and San Francisco Bay. Many Southern Californians, meanwhile, did not recognize the seriousness of the water issue, even though their water supply was imperiled by the unity of their northern neighbors, the courts and two severe droughts.

The result of this destructive squabbling, which at times approached warfare, was deadlock and inactivity. Two governors — Edmund G. Brown Jr. and George Deukmejian — tried to win approval for their differing water plans from the Legislature or the voters, but in vain. As for solving the delta problem, there has been little to show for the past 16 years of effort beyond mounds of studies, fading memories of hot debates over legislative bills and ballot propositions identified by numbers few people could recall a few years later.

This era began innocently enough when Edmund G. Brown Jr. became governor in 1975 and was persuaded to review the state's water resources development policy. "Jerry" Brown had inherited a state water project that had been championed and launched by his father and put into statewide operation by the Reagan administration. The state had built the framework of a huge water distribution system and signed contracts calling for the eventual delivery of 4.23 million acre-feet of water annually. But it didn't have all the facilities that would allow it to fulfill those contracts. The concept of a Peripheral Canal had been around for more than a dozen years; it had been nine years since it had been identified as the best answer for a transdelta facility. But Brown determined the state should take a fresh look at the Sacramento-San Joaquin Delta, its problems and all possible solutions to these questions. Meanwhile, the environmental movement was gaining support and becoming a political force with which to be reckoned. Before proceeding with a canal, the governor wanted water planners to study the effects conservation and reclamation would have on California's future demands for water.

uiet day of fishing along the delta shores

This examination evolved into a two-year series of studies under the guidance of Ronald Robie, Brown's choice to head the Department of Water Resources. Robie was a former vice chairman of the State Water Resources

Conservation was the watchword of 1976/77.

Control Board, who had twice been appointed to that board by two-term Republican governor, Ronald Reagan. "There were a lot of questions raised when the Environmental Impact Report on the Peripheral Canal was issued in 1974 [by the Reagan administration]," said Robie. "There was a storm of protest because there was no clear commitment to delta protection and guarantees. We did the review because I felt we needed to take stock of the criticisms to see whether there were things that should be changed. I wanted to have a current evaluation to be sure we had the right alternative."

Ultimately, when the review process was completed in early 1977, Robie's findings sustained previous conclusions: the canal was the best choice. As he explained, "It was the only sound facility that could guarantee protection for the delta and allow the state to meet its contract commitments."

Based on these studies, DWR designed a plan for the governor that recommended completion of the first phase of the State Water Project to ensure California's meeting its water needs through the turn of the century. The plan advocated building the Peripheral Canal as a joint federal-state effort since both entities had projects that drew water from the delta. At the same time, DWR took the position that construction of the canal shouldn't start until the federal government was willing to work with the state to maintain a guaranteed level of delta water quality. The Bureau of

Reclamation, which operates the Central Valley Project, had been doing this on a voluntary basis for a number of years although it had never formally agreed to operate in such a manner.

THE EXTREMELY DRY CONDITIONS BECAME A STAPLE OF EVENING NEWSCASTS AND PAGE ONE NEWSPAPER STORIES.

In an unexpected strategy, Brown decided to take his program to the state Legislature for approval. This was surprising because the Burns-Porter Act had clearly called for a delta facility as part of the State Water Project, and DWR, under his father's governorship, had chosen the Peripheral Canal as that facility. The young governor, however, felt a new legislative mandate of some sort was necessary because the Peripheral Canal had raised so much northern opposition during the Environmental Impact Report process conducted during the Reagan years.

Additionally, water was gaining interest as a statewide public issue because of the brief but intense 1976-77 drought. The extremely dry conditions, the worst the state had experienced since the 1930s, became a staple of evening newscasts and page one newspaper stories. Water rationing was imposed in many parts of the state and an emergency connection was hooked up to parched Marin County, north of San Francisco. Metropolitan voluntarily gave up most of the water it had planned to take from the State Water Project in 1977 so it could be used in areas of greater need north of the Tehachapis. To make up for that loss, Metropolitan operated every available pump on its Colorado River Aqueduct, running the system beyond its designed capacity to provide water for Southern California. At the same time, Metropolitan, which previously had operated largely out of the spotlight, put on a more public face, staging a near $1 million advertising campaign to promote water conservation in the Southland.

In 1977, Lake Oroville provided grim testimony to drought conditions.

So, at a high point of drought-induced public awareness, in February 1977, California began a five-year roller coaster ride on the fortunes of the Peripheral Canal. That month state Senator Ruben Ayala, chairman of the Agriculture and Water Committee, introduced legislation calling for construction of the canal, Senate Bill 346. Meanwhile, the governor was at work trying to persuade urban water agencies, environmental organizations and representatives of agriculture to join together in a spirit of compromise around the plan drafted by Robie and the Department of Water Resources. Four months later, portions of the DWR plan were grafted onto Ayala's original bill and SB 346 won swift approval in the Senate.

It was a different story in the Assembly, where the bill was in for a rough ride. Numerous amendments, tacked on before it passed, were returned to the Senate for concurrence, where, by this time, opposition was mounting, and the uneasy and delicate consensus the governor had sought to build was collapsing. There was a growing attitude that federal participation shouldn't be required to build the canal. Some senators switched their earlier votes and SB 346 died in the Senate, falling six votes short of that required for passage. In 1978, Brown and Ayala twice attempted to resuscitate SB 346, but neither effort proved successful.

Senator Ayala was a hard man to deter. In the final year of the decade, he introduced another bill, SB 200, which on close inspection emerged as a clone of the essential elements of the unsuccessful SB 346. It still called for the Peripheral Canal to be built jointly by California and the federal government. Shared construction seemed a remote possibility because the Washington, D.C. political climate was adverse. Ayala's new bill floundered. It held no hope of passage until the consensus group, which originally had been organized by the governor for efforts on SB 346, was reactivated. This time, under the leadership of Metropolitan's board chairman, Earle C. Blais, the bill would contain new language. It would be a state-only project.

"Up to this point, all the Peripheral Canal bills called for a joint project, but the consensus group came to the conclusion that we'd never get a joint-project bill through the Legislature," explained Blais. "We felt, however, that once we built the canal, the federal government would have to come in either as a partner or as a customer with the state transporting federal water for a charge."

In May 1979, SB 200 was amended; the new language specified a state-only Peripheral Canal as the delta-transfer facility in the Burns-Porter Act. Other provisions of the bill called for studies to create more storage facilities, relocation of the Contra Costa Canal intake to improve water quality and permitted the state to participate in studies to raise the height of Shasta Dam on the Sacramento River, another additional storage effort.

As for water quality issues, SB 200 provisions required the Peripheral Canal to be operated in a manner protecting the delta and mitigating some of the existing problems. In addition, the bill called for the state to study San Francisco Bay to make sure future exports from the delta would not prove detrimental to the bay. Lying immediately west of the delta, Suisun Marsh also would be granted protection against further saltwater intrusion with the construction of facilities to bring additional freshwater into this rich wildlife area.

Suisun, a marshy labyrinth of bays, sloughs, drainage channels and ponds

Drafting a new version of SB 200 was one thing; pushing it through the Legislature was another. Though the Senate Water and Agriculture Committee quickly approved the measure, it was stalled in the Finance Committee for six months before finally reaching the full Senate in January 1980, where it quickly passed. Quick agreement hopes were soundly dashed in the Assembly where the Water, Parks and Wildlife Committee haggled over SB 200 for six more months without approving it. Committee chairman Lawrence Kapiloff supported the bill but wanted amendments that would, among other things, provide stronger environmental protections and promote water conservation. Supporters of SB 200 opposed any changes, fearing a replay of 1977 when the original Peripheral Canal bill had been amended to death.

Kapiloff averted a stalemate with a compromise solution in the form of a proposed constitutional amendment, which added new guarantees to guard the Sacramento-San Joaquin Delta and strengthened protection from development for the Klamath, Trinity, Eel and Smith rivers on

HE TIRED, TROUBLING NORTH-SOUTH SPLIT INTENSIFIED. EMOTIONS RAN HIGH AGAINST THE PERIPHERAL CANAL IN THE NORTH.

California's north coast. Carrying about 30 percent of California's runoff, these rivers already had been designated part of the state's wild and scenic rivers system, where they were shielded from development. The amendment, which was destined to become Proposition 8 on the November 1980 ballot, was a shadow to SB 200. The two pieces of legislation were managed to move out of committee together and the amendment, if approved by the voters, would be incorporated in the state constitution only if SB 200 became law. The compromise held, and the two measures cleared the Assembly in late June.

The following month, Governor Brown signed SB 200 into law, simultaneously clearing the way for construction of the Peripheral Canal and

The Klamath River

further splitting the state on the issue. The governor had attempted to appease canal opponents by issuing an executive order calling for water conservation and reclamation and asking the federal government to put the north coast rivers under federal protection. Canal opponents remained adamant against any kind of delta facility and, on the same evening SB 200 was signed by the governor, they announced plans to seek a referendum against building the Peripheral Canal. Brown, to the surprise of many, determined he would become neutral and leave the issue to the voters. Many supporters of the water bill felt the governor, by taking this position, had deserted them and weakened the case for passing Proposition 8.

Governor Edmund G. Brown Jr.

Nearly two more years were to pass before the fate of SB 200 was finally resolved. Early on, battle lines were clearly drawn, with canal foes immediately collecting signatures to force a Peripheral Canal referendum. Their successful effort, by October 1980, qualified the referendum for an election to be called by the governor. Meanwhile, a heated campaign over Proposition 8, supported by Metropolitan's board, was winding down. A month later, California voters went to the polls, registering their approval of both delta protection and safeguards for the north coast rivers by a 54-46 percent margin. Proposition 8 had passed, but wouldn't become a part of the constitution unless SB 200 went into effect.

The final act of the Peripheral Canal drama unfolded around Proposition 9 — as the referendum was designated when SB 200 opponents turned in the required number of qualified signatures. Though canal supporters, for strategic purposes, wanted Governor Brown to call a special election on the issue during 1981, he refused. The measure then had to wait for the next regular statewide ballot in June, 1982.

Meanwhile, the tired, troubling north-south split intensified. Emotions ran high against the Peripheral Canal in the north and the old cry, "Don't let them take our water" once more was heard. Environmentalists railed against the canal proclaiming the bill did not provide sufficient protection for the delta. And then a "strange bedfellow" alliance developed. The environmentalists acquired new partners in fighting the referendum when two of the San Joaquin Valley's largest agribusinesses — the J.G. Boswell Company and the Salyer Land Company — joined their cause, but, as was widely publicized, for reasons diametrically opposite those of their new environmentalist allies. Reported by the San Francisco Chronicle, the Los Angeles Times and a number of other newspapers, these landholders contended the legislation was burdened with environmental safeguards under which too much water would be released to maintain delta water quality and, therefore, keep Central Valley farms from getting enough water. The safeguards to which they referred were included in the proposition itself and in the constitutional guarantees provided by the 1980 voter-approved Proposition 8, which locked the gate on the north coast rivers. In any case, it cannot be doubted that the substantial contributions from these unexpected sources played a major role in the opposition's campaign to defeat the Peripheral Canal measure. The full impact of the Boswell-Salyer participation can only be surmised.

In Southern California, Proposition 9 failed to capture widespread strong support; it certainly didn't generate anything like the stormy Northern California emotional climate. Finally, in June of 1982, this two-decade-long saga of the Peripheral Canal came to an end at the ballot box with its stunning defeat. Droves of Northern Californians rushed to polling places to vote against Proposition 9 in unprecedented majorities: San Francisco County voted 95 percent against it; Contra Costa County recorded 96 percent opposed; and Marin County was a near-unanimous 97 percent no. Though Southern California voted for Proposition 9 with a respectable 63-percent-yes vote, it came nowhere near producing the majorities necessary to offset the tidal wave of northern no votes. The Peripheral Canal was soundly defeated by a 62-38 percent margin, leaving California with no solution to its delta woes or means of fulfilling its contracts for water from the State Water Project.

Looking back at the defeat of Proposition 9, Pat Brown, who had made the State Water Project a political reality with his determined leadership, pithily summed up the situation: "Southern California didn't have the enthusiasm to put the Peripheral Canal over and no politician with any statewide status was fighting for it. Northern California was enthusiastically against it."

The Proposition 9 campaign was the last hurrah in the water arena for the administration of Jerry Brown, who did not seek a third term in 1982. That fall, George Deukmejian, who had been a canal supporter, was elected governor and the search for a delta solution turned away from the Peripheral Canal. The new governor appointed veteran water engineer David N. Kennedy, then Metropolitan's assistant general manager, as his director of the Department of Water Resources in 1983. Under Kennedy, DWR shifted its focus back to the delta interior in search of solutions for the state's continuing water problems, and by the end of the year, had produced a plan of improvements in the northern and southern portions of the delta that evolved into the Deukmejian administration's legislative water package in 1984. The primary feature was the 12-mile New Hope Cross Channel, a new waterway that would help move flows more efficiently. Other elements of the "through-delta-facility" program called for widening some existing channels in the south delta and the installation of four additional pumps at the State Water Project's delta pumping plant.

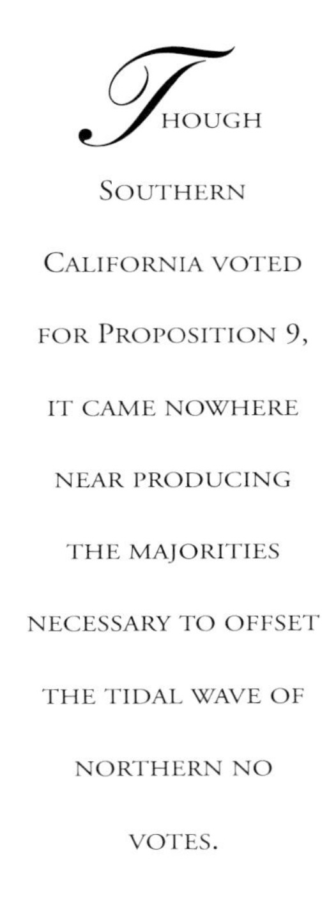

Though Southern California voted for Proposition 9, it came nowhere near producing the majorities necessary to offset the tidal wave of northern no votes.

In retrospect, the Deukmejian plan had little prospect of success. From the start, it was caught in a withering political cross fire — the Democratic Legislature wasn't willing to hand a Republican governor an easy water victory and the north-south schism over water remained alive and kicking. But perhaps most telling of all was the derisive nickname, "Duke's Ditch," that was attached to the New Hope Cross Channel. At this juncture, Senator Ruben Ayala picked up the governor's package, introducing it as SB 1369. In its original form, water agencies such as Metropolitan viewed the bill as an interim rather than final solution to delta problems and cautiously endorsed it. But after a flood of amendments obliterated the intent of the legislation, its support — lukewarm at best — evaporated quickly. The bill died in committee.

The following year, Assemblyman Jim Costa attempted to resurrect many of the elements of the governor's proposal with the backing of environmental organizations and water contractors. His bill, AB 1710, floundered

Governor George Deukmejian

Governor Pete Wilson

in the face of continued Northern California opposition which now centered around a new issue — an asserted but unsubstantiated charge that water diversions were causing serious environmental damage to San Francisco Bay. This emotional allegation prevailed and Costa's bill failed to clear the Assembly, ending the final attempt to get a water bill through the Legislature during the Deukmejian administration.

Following that defeat, the administration adopted a new strategy. DWR would move ahead one step at a time. In 1986, the slow process of preparing Environmental Impact Reports on three packages began: improvements in the north delta, the south delta and construction of Los Banos Grandes Reservoir. The latter would be a 1.7 million-acre-foot lake in the San Joaquin Valley designed to provide storage capacity to hold heavy winter flows that would otherwise rush through the delta. Final work on the three EIRs was expected to be completed by the end of 1990, but the decision to go ahead with any or all of them would rest with the new administration of Governor Pete Wilson.

The state also moved ahead on two other projects: expansion of the East Branch of the California Aqueduct (with Metropolitan's concurrence) and the creation of the Kern Water Bank. The east branch enlargement, a $350 million program scheduled to be completed in 1992, will enable the district to receive more of its state water entitlement. The Kern Water Bank was an outgrowth of Metropolitan explorations to expand its water supply. However, once its scope and complexity were realized, the Department of Water Resources stepped in. The water bank will allow the state to store surplus water in a groundwater basin near Bakersfield for use in dry years when it can be pumped from the ground. DWR's initial goal will be storage of 1 million acre-feet of water; however, the program eventually could be expanded to as much as 3 million acre-feet.

"Unless the Legislature and the governor are making proclamations, people think nothing is happening," observed Kennedy. "Our perception is that the Legislature has passed a comprehensive water bill, the Burns-Porter Act. We have taken the authority we have and gone ahead step by step. This is a more polarized state than it was 30 years ago and you can't have an internal debate on water politically. Water is like an ethics issue, and people are just not open-minded about it."

At the close of the Deukmejian era and the opening of the final decade of the century, California found itself in a perilous position. Two administrations had floundered over the issues of the delta and improving the yield of the State Water Project while the state was experiencing unprecedented population growth. At the close of this period, drought once again hit California. Five consecutive dry years extending through the winter of 1990-91 devastated the state. The drought was so serious that parched residents of Santa Barbara, not being allowed to water their lawns, spray-painted their dead grass green, and the city of San Francisco, perhaps the most implacable of State Water Project foes, very quietly hooked up to the state system for emergency transfers.

Widening the California Aqueduct's East Branch

In Southern California, Metropolitan viewed the future with some misgivings. Although during the 1980s, its water deliveries to its member agencies nearly doubled, all three of the region's water importation systems were shackled by the end of the decade. The city of Los Angeles was restricted by court orders and related agreements in its operation of the Los Angeles Aqueduct from the Owens Valley and Mono Basin. The $3.5 billion Central Arizona Project was completed to Phoenix, and MWD's firm allotment of Colorado River water accordingly shrank by more than 600,000 acre-feet a year. The State Water Project, as envisioned and planned, remained a functional but severely incomplete system.

Chapter 13

STRETCHING THE SUPPLY

Water isn't elastic. But it is surprising how far a water supply can be stretched with creativity and resourcefulness — qualities upon which Southern California water leaders increasingly relied in the 1980s. And they seem destined to play an even more important role in the years ahead.

In the final decade of the 20th century, the Southland finds itself in an uncomfortable and vulnerable position. It is a highly developed area without an adequate, dependable water supply. All three of the great water importation systems built to serve Southern California — the Los Angeles Aqueduct, the Colorado River Aqueduct and the State Water Project — are truncated in some significant way. Although each was built to supplement the area's local water supply, not one is able to deliver the amount of water it was designed to carry or for which contracts were signed.

Much of the work of Southern California's water visionaries has seemingly unraveled. In 1985, the $3.5 billion Central Arizona Project, one result of the resolution of the *Arizona vs. California* controversy, went on line. As water began to flow east, then south, then east again to Phoenix (the project would be completed to Tucson in the 1990s), Metropolitan lost, on a dependable basis, access to more than 660,000 acre-feet of water from the Colorado River. Aware of this eventuality since the Supreme Court ruling in 1963, Metropolitan had the following year turned to the State Water

Project to make up the shortfall and increased its contract for northern water by 500,000 acre-feet; subsequently, with the annexation of West Covina in 1965, that contracted amount was again increased — to an ultimate 2,011,500 acre-feet a year. However, the state has failed to provide the additional storage and conveyance facilities necessary to deliver MWD's entitlement. The project is stalemated between conflicting political forces and remains deficient, having a capacity to deliver about 2.3 million acre-feet annually, but contractual obligations of some 4.2 million acre-feet. Compounding the problem, even Metropolitan's remaining 550,000 acre-foot entitlement to the use of Colorado River water is threatened by renewed litigation in *Arizona vs. California.* Nearly three decades since the Supreme Court decision, there is pending litigation in the original case which has been reinstituted on behalf of Indian tribal claimants.

The project is stalemated between conflicting political forces and remains deficient. Compounding the problem, Metropolitan's remaining entitlement to the use of Colorado River water is threatened.

On another front, the city of Los Angeles' water supply from the Owens Valley and Mono Basin has come under a barrage of legal and contractual restraints, actions which have significantly altered the city's historical pattern of water use and, in turn, burdened Metropolitan. Before an agreement with Inyo County and injunctions and lawsuits restricted Los Angeles' exports, the city typically purchased about 50,000 acre-feet a year from Metropolitan and drew about 470,000 acre-feet through its aqueduct system. In 1990, L.A.'s purchase of water from Metropolitan mushroomed to 440,000 acre-feet.

Still another threat to Southern California's water security has been the discovery of contamination in almost all its major groundwater basins. Overpumping, saltwater intrusion from the Pacific and a new enemy, chemical contamination (mostly solvents used in manufacturing during World War II), emerged as gremlins in a groundwater system which has traditionally provided the Southland with about one-third of its water.

A discouraging picture at best; however, a bright side to water resources

Metropolitan's conservation message being spread at county fairs

development in Southern California appeared in the mid-1980s. Ingenuity was the key word as Metropolitan, under the leadership of its newly appointed general manager, Carl Boronkay, began an intensive search for new ways to augment the region's water supply. A historic and innovative water conservation agreement between Metropolitan and the Imperial Irrigation District became the cornerstone of this effort. Though it took some five years of negotiations to work out the details of the agreement, when it was finalized in 1989, Metropolitan had secured the first major new supply of water for Southern California in decades. Moreover, it could be the prototype for additional agreements for water from that source.

Metropolitan's search uncovered a number of non-traditional ways to stretch supplies and find new water sources: groundwater storage and water banking agreements with a number of water agencies; other conservation programs in the Coachella and Imperial valleys; Metropolitan's local projects subsidy program which has encouraged California's most active water reclamation effort; conservation efforts by member agencies and the public; and a renewed look at the technology of desalination. In addition, MWD has adopted a strong water transfer policy. Not only did the district participate in the governor's drought emergency water bank (which allowed agricultural water to be "sold" to urban water users through the Department of Water Resources), but it is pursuing efforts that would enable direct short- or long-term purchases of water that is currently put to agricultural use.

Though innovative programs are resulting in wise and prudent uses of water resources, they can be excruciatingly difficult to negotiate. The landmark Metropolitan-Imperial Irrigation District water conservation agreement is a case in point. The roots of the pact date back more than 30 years to the *Arizona vs. California* litigation. U.S Supreme Court Special Master Simon Rifkind noted, in a report to the court, that water was being wasted, particularly unused runoff flowing into the Salton Sea from Imperial Valley land supplied with water by the Imperial Irrigation District. Although the federal government completed studies and issued a report on water conservation opportunities, the idea of salvaging water in the Imperial Valley languished for two decades.

Las Virgenes MWD'S Tapia reclamation plant in a secluded corner of the Santa Monica Mountains — since 1983 included in Metropolitan's local projects program

The issue resurfaced in 1980, when an Imperial Valley farmer accused IID of negligent irrigation practices causing flooding of his land along the Salton Sea. Asked to investigate the complaint, the state Department of Water Resources the following year issued a report confirming that, while IID had improved its operations, it still was wasting water. The irrigation district was directed to prepare a conservation plan, but demurred, whereupon the issue was bucked up to the State Water Resources Control Board. Following hearings, the state board in June 1984 concluded that Imperial was misusing water as it had failed to implement additional conservation measures. Ordered by the SWRCB to prepare a broad conservation plan to conserve at least 100,000 acre-feet a year, IID challenged the decision in the state courts, but, bowing to the inevitable, invited Metropolitan to discuss a conservation agreement.

The purpose for such an agreement was straightforward: Imperial needed to implement conservation methods such as lining earthen canals with concrete. Since the irrigation district's distribution system consisted of nearly 1,600 miles of main and lateral delivery canals, many unlined, the opportunities for saving water were substantial. Metropolitan would pay the costs of such improvements and, in turn, be guaranteed the water calculated to be saved. Reaching agreement, as straightforward as the plan appeared, turned out to be tortuous.

General Manager Boronkay reflected, "Substantial time was spent getting to know one another, the problems and objectives of each side, and the local political considerations bearing on the proposed agreement." Imperial's general manager, Chuck Shreves, said of the bargaining: "We can conserve water and we recognize that fact and that we are a part of California. But it is also important to understand that people are very proprietary when it comes to water."

Metropolitan's negotiating team was particularly strengthened by Assistant General Manager Myron Holburt who had served for 16 years as chief engineer of the state's Colorado River Board before joining MWD. Holburt quickly felt the depth of that proprietary feeling and the divisive nature of water in the Imperial Valley. "Some farmers didn't understand that their water use wouldn't be cut and that IID was only giving up the water that was conserved," said Holburt. "There also were those who were just uneasy about the deal and some who simply wanted to sell water for a lot of money."

Canal lining in Imperial Valley — a conservation measure

Negotiations between the two agencies began in June 1984, and the first major obstacle to deal with was the fundamental difference of the parties as to what was to be negotiated. Some of Imperial's representatives simply wanted Metropolitan to buy their water, leaving IID free to use the proceeds for conservation measures or otherwise. Thus they wished to negotiate only the quantity and price of water. Metropolitan made it clear that it would not concede any right of Imperial to sell water outside its service area and that it would negotiate only the costs of conservation projects. MWD prevailed on this issue, but the concept of selling water haunted the negotiations throughout. A related stumbling block was Imperial's concern that such a conservation agreement with Metropolitan would undermine its legal contention that it had the right to sell conserved water to San Diego and even areas of Kern County. This obstacle was removed when both parties agreed to expressly preserve their respective legal positions so that the conservation agreement would be neutral on that question.

Imperial Valley Farm

MWD's board approved the agreement, but the Imperial board voted to hold public hearings instead of validating the draft.

Another concern of Imperial was that, on the one hand, it was being pressed by Metropolitan and the state board to save water that wasted to the Salton Sea, while on the other hand, some observers were predicting that such action would have an adverse effect upon the sea's health. This issue was resolved when Imperial and Metropolitan supported successful legislation that protects Imperial from liability for effects on the Salton Sea resulting from conservation measures within IID.

Within 13 months of the start of negotiations, a draft agreement was reached and scheduled for ratification by the boards of directors of both agencies on the same day. Metropolitan's board approved the agreement, but the Imperial board voted to hold public hearings instead of validating the draft. Three months later in October 1985, Imperial's board by a 3-to-2 vote rejected the agreement, some members bowing to local sentiment that IID "wasn't going to get enough money."

Imperial's position was temporarily bolstered by a 1985 state Superior Court ruling to the effect that the State Water Resources Control Board lacked the authority to enforce its decision calling for IID to draft and implement a water conservation program. However, that ruling was overturned the following year by a state Court of Appeals decision. By this time, nearly two years of sporadic, fruitless negotiations had passed. In 1988, the Superior Court upheld the merits of the SWRCB's decision and later in the year the board ordered Imperial to devise a plan that would save 100,000 acre-feet of water a year by the beginning of 1994.

Lester Bornt signs agreement for IID as General Manager Carl Boronkay waits to sign for MWD.

In the spring of 1988, IID had retained Robert Edmonston, a well-known consulting engineer, and reopened talks with MWD. In November of that year, Imperial's board, under the leadership of its president, Lester Bornt, finally approved a conservation agreement. The following month Metropolitan's board concurred, and both districts received congratulations from such diverse interests as environmental organizations, engineering societies, irrigation associations and political leaders. Demonstrative of the highly charged political situation connected with the negotiations, of the five IID board members serving at the start of negotiations, only one remained in office by the time the agreement was signed. And the chairman who signed for IID was defeated in the next board election.

One last and unexpected hurdle arose in 1989 when Coachella Valley Water District sought an injunction to block the conservation agreement. Coachella, which holds higher priority rights to the use of Colorado River water than does Metropolitan, wanted first claim on any water saved as a result of the conservation agreement. Coachella sought this concession because its water rights are junior to Imperial's and Coachella would have to take the first cuts if ever there were a requirement to reduce agricultural use because of water shortages. Eventually, this and several lesser differences were ironed out, giving Coachella limited rights to the conserved water, and a supplemental water conservation agreement was approved in December 1989.

Testing a unique technology that would allow lining of the Coachella Canal while water still flows

The final agreement, difficult as it may have been to achieve, benefited both parties. Metropolitan wound up with 106,110 acre-feet of water annually for 35 years — except under the limited circumstances under the Supreme Court's 1964 decree when Imperial, Coachella and/or Palo Verde Irrigation District would have to reduce their use of Colorado River water. To make conservation improvements on Imperial's distribution system estimated to save that amount of water, MWD agreed to fund nearly $98 million in capital costs; $23 million in indirect costs including loss of hydroelectric power revenue, loss of revenue from reduced water deliveries, any mitigation of adverse effects on agriculture from increased salinity, and others; and $2.6 million annually in direct costs such as operation, maintenance and replacement of structural projects, repair of any damage to the project, ongoing costs of nonstructural aspects of the program, and a number of other items.

This work includes the lining of more than 300 miles of major delivery and lateral canals, plus construction of regulatory reservoirs and lateral interceptors, ditches that will catch excess water and divert it into reservoirs for downstream use. Distribution system automation, installation of non-leak gates, and implementation of a more efficient distribution system and on-farm water management practices are also included. This agreement, expected to be a prototype for additional conservation accords with IID, has been cited throughout the United States and abroad as an enlightened approach, indeed a model, for making more effective use of limited water supplies.

Other efforts to creatively augment water supplies have been somewhat easier to achieve. A conservation program involving the lining of 66 miles of the All-American and Coachella canals in Riverside and Imperial counties won Congressional approval in 1988. Completing the lining of these

Metropolitan releases water into Whitewater River to be carried to Coachella's spreading grounds.

canals is expected to conserve 100,000 acre-feet of water a year, an amount potentially available to Metropolitan. In addition, MWD, Coachella and the federal Bureau of Reclamation are testing a unique technology on a mile-and-a-half stretch of the Coachella Canal that allows a plastic lining and concrete cover to be applied to earthen canals while water is still flowing through the channel. The five-year job of lining reaches of the All-American and Coachella canals is scheduled to start in 1992.

Metropolitan, in cooperation with Coachella and the Desert Water Agency, developed the concept of interagency groundwater storage and exchange programs in Southern California in 1967. All three agencies have contracts for deliveries from the State Water Project, but Coachella and Desert never built the costly connections to hook up to the state's California Aqueduct. Instead, Metropolitan has been taking delivery of those agencies' state water and providing them, in return, an equal amount of Colorado River water.

The program, and subsequent ones modeled after it, operates in a manner similar to a bank account. In times of plenty, water is stored in underground basins for later use as needed. In 1984, a Metropolitan-Coachella-Desert advance-delivery agreement took advantage of surplus flows on the Colorado River and the availability of power from Hoover and Parker dams, allowing storage supplies to be pumped through the Colorado River Aqueduct during the mid-1980s. To handle these extra flows, Metropolitan also appropriated $4 million to expand Coachella's groundwater spreading basins north of Palm Springs. Water is released from the Colorado River Aqueduct into the Whitewater River which carries it to the spreading grounds. From there, the water filters into a vast groundwater basin beneath the Palm Springs area from which Desert and Coachella draw water. Nearly 600,000 acre-feet of water was deposited. Deliveries stopped in 1987 with the onset of another statewide drought, but Metropolitan was able to continue to take the two agencies' entitlement water from the State Water Project to augment supplies for coastal Southern California.

THE PROGRAM OPERATES IN A MANNER SIMILAR TO A BANK ACCOUNT.

Since 1986, Metropolitan has attempted to establish a similar storage agreement involving up to 800,000 acre-feet of water with the Arvin-Edison Water Storage District in the southeastern San Joaquin Valley. This banking exchange has been complicated by questions: How might it affect deliveries of water to other State Water Project contractors? Are there concerns because water from the federal Central Valley Project is involved? Then too, environmental organizations, while praising the idea of the exchange, also have questioned its possible detrimental effects on the Sacramento-San Joaquin Delta.

Under the proposed agreement, which has been submitted to the SWRCB for approval, Metropolitan would deliver up to 130,000 acre-feet of its state project water to Arvin-Edison during wet years and would invest $20 million to build spreading basins to help recharge sorely overdrafted groundwater supplies in the valley. (To further aid in the latter effort, Arvin-Edison also could use some surface deliveries to irrigate crops instead of pumping water from the ground.) In dry years, Arvin-Edison would pump water banked in the ground for its use, while Metropolitan would take from 90,000 to 125,000 acre-feet of water from A-E's Central Valley Project supplies.

Within its own service area, Metropolitan has groundwater storage agreements with some member agencies and subagencies which also stretch water supplies available to the Southland during dry periods. Groundwater storage accounts with the Chino Basin and Upper San Gabriel Valley municipal water districts were developed for use during shortages. In 1990, Metropolitan also launched studies to examine the potential of groundwater storage programs in basins near Moorpark in Ventura County, Hemet in Riverside County, and the northern edge of the Marine Corps' Camp Pendleton in Orange and San Diego counties.

Landscaping a Southland freeway: watering will make use of reclaimed supplies.

In 1982, Metropolitan introduced the local projects program challenging member agencies to attempt innovative water reclamation efforts. Under this program, MWD currently provides its member agencies a financial incentive of $154 for each acre-foot of water they treat and reuse. By the end of 1990, 23 reclamation projects were in operation, with a total ultimate annual yield of more than 60,000 acre-feet of reusable water. The district is evaluating another eight projects, its board of directors having established a goal of reclaiming 150,000 acre-feet a year by the turn of the century. The vast majority of this reclaimed water is used for landscape irrigation and groundwater basin recharge, freeing potable water that would otherwise be used for these purposes.

Energy plays a two-fold role in Metropolitan's distribution of water in Southern California, with substantial amounts of power necessary to pump water over mountains into Southern California and to pump it out of groundwater basins. Metropolitan's active public conservation and in-school water education programs not only help save badly needed water but, in turn, that saving reduces energy use as well. Having been the world leader in developing small hydroelectric power generating plants on water distribution systems, Metropolitan today has 14 such power plants, producing enough power to serve 82,000 homes and saving the equivalent of three-quarters-of-a-million barrels of oil annually. This power is recovered from water coursing downhill through Metropolitan's distribution lines: water, which previously flowed through special valves to decrease pressure, now goes through turbines which create energy and dissipate the pressure. The novel idea of recovering potential power that was otherwise being wasted became more economically attractive when the energy crisis and Arab oil embargo of the mid-1970s drove power costs sky-high. Of concern, however, was the prospect of lengthy delays in submitting to the permit procedures of the Federal Power Commission. So Metropolitan decided to test that agency's claim to jurisdiction. While the issue was pending in court, however, the district's general counsel, Robert P. Will, obtained the commission's agreement to legislation abbreviating the permit procedure. Metropolitan's initial application became the model used by others.

MWD's first small hydro plant began operation in December 1979 on a pipeline near the Burbank Airport. Thirteen more plants were on line by 1985 and more are in Metropolitan's future. Design work on the Etiwanda Power Plant in Rancho Cucamonga is under way, with construction expected to begin in early 1992. This 24-megawatt plant will be the largest on Metropolitan's distribution system.

A fresh look at desalination as a possible way of augmenting Southern California water supplies came to the forefront in 1990. Converting ocean or brackish water into that which is potable has been technologically feasible for some time, but its costs have been considered prohibitive, far more expensive than traditional water sources. To continue its pursuit of innovations in water supply, in 1990 Metropolitan's board of directors authorized a $500,000 study to find potential sites for a demonstration desalting plant near existing conventional power plants along the Southern California coast. Metropolitan hopes to design, build and operate a demonstration plant within five years that would be capable of producing between 5 and

Desalination is getting a fresh look.

10 million gallons of freshwater daily. Additionally, the district is participating in a study to site a large desalting plant in Baja California just south of the Mexican border to supply water for both regions.

Vast changes have swept across Southern California in the half century since Metropolitan began delivering supplemental water in 1941. Population growth surpassed all expectations; today the politics of water is even more instrumental than the engineering. At the same time, the Southland's dependence on the water that Metropolitan delivers has substantially increased. Where and how Metropolitan will obtain the water necessary to sustain one of the world's most productive economies, today's 15 million people and the millions more expected is an issue clouded by uncertainty. One certain thing, however, is that innovation will continue to play an integral role in this odyssey.

Chapter 14

A TASTE OF QUALITY

Half a century ago, when Metropolitan began supplying water to Southern California, most people didn't think much about water at all, let alone its quality. It should taste good and it should be there when one turned on the tap. But times change — and along with them, priorities. Across the United States, concerns about drinking-water supplies emerged as part of the broad spectrum of environmental questions that were raised in the 1970s and '80s, and new federal and state regulations were enacted governing water quality. Amid news reports of pesticide runoff from agriculture and chemical dumping by industry, people today are vitally interested in the caliber of the water they consume, and Metropolitan goes to great lengths to ensure the high quality of the water it provides.

THE DISTRICT FINE-TUNED ITS TECHNOLOGICAL TESTING TO BECOME STATE-OF-THE-ART IN ACHIEVING THE COMMITMENT IT HAS MADE TO QUALITY.

In the early 1980s, the district fine-tuned its technological testing to become state-of-the-art in achieving the commitment it has made to quality. Relying on a system that is both "high tech" and "high taste," modern techniques such as gas chromatography/mass spectrometry allow contaminants to be detected in quantities as minute as parts per trillion. At the same time, Metropolitan considers taste to be extremely important, and for that there is no substitute for the trained human palate. Borrowing an idea long used in the food and beverage industries, the district established tasting panels to help monitor water quality. Though they obviously can't uniformly match high tech's minute-quantity-detection achievements, these Metropolitan laboratory employees can detect certain impurities in water at levels as low as a few parts per trillion.

Back in 1941, technology wasn't available to detect impurities in such ultra-low amounts. Therefore, such potential health hazards in water as trihalomethanes had yet to be discovered. In fact, Metropolitan's principal water quality concern at that time was the high level of hardness of the water delivered through the Colorado River Aqueduct. So, to remove some of the hardness, Metropolitan built a water softening plant in La Verne (later named after F. E. Weymouth, the organization's first general manager and chief engineer). The district continued to soften water until the 1970s when it began to receive supplies from Northern California through the State Water Project — water containing far less dissolved salts that when blended with the Colorado River supply, produced a more palatable product. Thus, the need for softening was eliminated.

Chlorination also has been a standard part of Metropolitan's treatment process since 1941. Today taken for granted as a means of controlling such deadly water-borne diseases as cholera, hepatitis and typhoid fever, chlorination has been used for decades. The American patent was issued to an Albert Leeds of New Jersey in 1888. But it wasn't until 1902 that the first continuous use of chlorine as a water disinfectant began in the Belgian town of Middelkerke. Over its 50 years of supplying water, Metropolitan has used either free chlorine or chloramines — a blend of chlorine and ammonia — to disinfect and control bacteriological growth in water provided for domestic uses.

Chlorine being transferred to filtration plant storage tanks from 17-ton chlorine tanker

It wasn't until the mid-1970s, when water quality was becoming a national concern, that trihalomethanes (THMs) came to light — discovered almost simultaneously by a team of Environmental Protection Agency researchers and a Danish researcher. THMs, compounds formed as byproducts of chlorine disinfection, are created when chlorine reacts with such dissolved decaying organic material as leaves, bark and other plant matter in water. Of the four THMs, one, chloroform, was directly linked to cancer in animal studies. The other three — dicholorobromomethane, dibromochloromethane and bromoform — also are suspected of being carcinogens.

Federal regulation of water quality began in 1974 when Congress passed the Safe Drinking Water Act, giving the Environmental Protection Agency authority to set and regulate water quality standards. EPA has since established standards for a variety of substances found in water. In 1979, the agency created a standard for THMs which water agencies were

Each year with more than 120,000 tests, Metropolitan checks for almost 200 different substances ranging from pesticides to disease-causing microbes.

required to meet by 1981. Later in 1986, the Safe Drinking Water Act was amended, greatly increasing EPA's regulatory activity. Standards had to be established for 83 new contaminants by 1989 and 25 new standards set every three years thereafter.

To meet the 1979 THM standard, Metropolitan altered its treatment process, switching from the use of free chlorine to chloramines. This was necessary because the Northern California water Metropolitan receives carries significant amounts of natural organics — mostly from delta farm drains — and bromides from the seawater that mixes with the freshwater as the rivers run toward San Francisco Bay. When delta water is disinfected, these organics and bromides react with chlorine to form THMs and other disinfection byproducts. Chloramination produces lower amounts of THMs. This treatment process has brought the level of THMs in the water that Metropolitan serves today to 50-60 parts per billion, well under federal requirements.

The aesthetics of water became a serious local concern for Metropolitan in 1979 and 1980, when the water in Lake Mathews, the terminal reservoir for the Colorado River Aqueduct in Riverside County, developed serious taste and odor problems — the earthy, musty smell of a damp basement, with a taste to match. At the time, Metropolitan had no tools with which to identify the problem and determine how to control it.

Eventually, after considerable research and consultations with experts in other parts of the country who had dealt with similar conditions, the culprit was identified — a blue-green algae growing in the bottom of the lake — and with the use of copper sulfate, the condition soon cleared up. The Lake Mathews incident prompted Metropolitan to embark upon an ambitious program to upgrade its capabilities, with water quality becoming a major thrust. The program included the establishment of reservoir monitoring, making use of scuba divers to collect water samples from below the surface and the creation of the water-tasting, flavor profile panel to provide human detectors who could help uncover subtle taste and odor problems. Metropolitan also committed to greatly improving its technical and analytical abilities by constructing and operating a sophisticated, modern water quality laboratory.

It was early 1980 and "high tech" was about to meet "high taste" in the name of water quality. The tasters work in the water quality division and do their sipping four mornings a week. As part of a panel, the tasters (at any given time, there are between six and 12 of them, each having undergone six weeks of special training) test samples drawn from all five of Metropolitan's treatment plants, its distribution system and its finished water reservoirs. As people tend to associate odors with things they've experienced, flavor profile characteristics have been established so all panel members can describe a taste or odor in a common language: geranium, fishy, grassy, musty or swampy, for example.

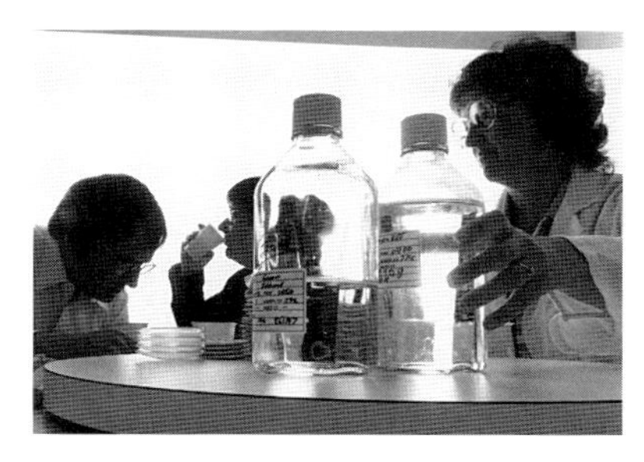

Human detectors test for taste and odor problems.

And two newcomers try their hands at the nose- and palate-sensitive work: then Senator Pete Wilson and his wife, Gayle, on a tour of the lab.

The heart of Metropolitan's efforts to safeguard water supplies is its 28,000-square-foot water quality laboratory built adjacent to the Weymouth filtration plant. Opened in April 1985, the $6 million state-of-the-art facility is widely considered to be one of the finest in the United States. This laboratory and smaller ones at Metropolitan's treatment plants operate 365 days a year. Each year with more than 120,000 tests, Metropolitan checks for almost 200 different substances ranging from pesticides to disease-causing microbes. Testing for some substances is done only once a year, but others must be monitored far more frequently. Daily tests are conducted for coliform bacteria because detection is a red flag indicating a bacterial problem. Experts analyze turbidity or clarity every two hours, with increased turbidity indicating material suspended in the water which may be harboring bacteria. Disinfectant residuals are monitored continuously. Additionally, Metropolitan tests for 22 different byproducts of its disinfection process, including the federally-regulated THMs.

While the water that Metropolitan now delivers is well within the standards

PEROXONE treatment could be the answer in meeting anticipated EPA standards.

issued by EPA, it may not be good enough in the years ahead. EPA is expected to adopt an array of even tougher water quality benchmarks, including those for THMs. The allowable THM limit of 100 parts per billion will be sliced in half. Consequently, Metropolitan and other water utilities around the country will have to use different disinfection processes to minimize the impacts of chloramination, or for those still using it, chlorination, which, ironically, less than a century ago was hailed as a boon to public health.

Identifying and implementing a new water treatment process became a primary task of Metropolitan's water quality division in the late 1980s. The district has been taking a hard look at three processes — granular activated carbon (GAC), ozone and PEROXONE (a combination of ozone and hydrogen peroxide).

PEROXONE started as a dark horse, an unknown, unproven disinfectant that many expected would end up an also-ran against other proven performers. However, pitted against its pricey rival, GAC, PEROXONE was a clear winner, especially in cost. Then, compared to ozone, it controlled taste and odor problems in the water better and was in a virtual dead heat on many other quality tests. GAC was the surprise loser in the competition. It was much more costly — estimates range from $700 million to $3 billion for a complete GAC retrofit of existing Metropolitan treatment plants. Still, GAC was expected to be one of the best methods for water purification; yet, even with treatment contact times triple that of the industry norm, it couldn't bring THM levels below 10 parts per billion (ppb). Conversely, PEROXONE routinely reduced THMs to 2 or 3 ppb. This made PEROXONE a relative bargain. An ozone treatment facility would cost around $300 million to install; PEROXONE installation would run roughly $200 million.

In 1989, it was decided to study PEROXONE in a demonstration-scale project in an effort to discover any potential drawbacks. A $13 million

Metropolitan's water quality laboratory is considered one of the finest in the nation.

facility would be constructed as part of a $23 million project to treat five million gallons of water a day. Ozone also would be tested in experiments that will closely resemble actual use.

The 1970s and '80s were truly decades of increasing regulatory activity, of a consumer sophistication previously unevidenced, of an unprecedented demand for technical expertise. They were decades of challenge spurring continuing expansion in the water quality arena.

Chapter 15

NEW CHALLENGES AND A NEW CENTURY

On June 17, 1991, Metropolitan proudly, though with no fanfare, marked 50 years of delivery of water from the Colorado River into Southern California. Ironically, at the same time, the state was suffering its fifth consecutive year of drought. Rationing had been a reality for most Southland communities for several months, and dry conditions throughout the state had forced Metropolitan to cut deliveries to its member agencies by nearly a third. The two major reservoirs on the incomplete State Water Project were precariously low.

By March 1, DWR had sent only 10 percent of Metropolitan's yearly order for state project water "over the hill" — as the Tehachapis are referred to by those in water circles — and MWD would be allowed only another 10 percent by the end of summer. Negotiations had progressed with the Secretary of the Interior and other Colorado River basin states that would assure a full aqueduct crossing the desert into Southern California — at least for the time being.

Communities districtwide strove to find the most fair way to pass the cuts on to consumers. This was the first real rationing that Southern Californians had ever seen. True, there had been voluntary cutbacks necessary in the 1976-77 drought, but this time changes in lifestyle were threatened. To further complicate decisions, consideration had to be given to the possibility of continued drought beyond this difficult fifth year.

And water leaders were particularly concerned, for not only were endless hours consumed with finding innovative ways to deal with unprecedented conditions, but no matter how they strained their eyes, none could see an unfaltering light at the end of the drought tunnel.

Yet this experience has contained an important lesson: Undue hardship that would be expected from such an extended drought was avoided as a result of the margin of safety in water and infrastructure provided by earlier district leaders.

In reflecting on the accomplishments of the last 50 years on that mid-June day, there were those who would wonder exactly what achievements Southern Californians would be celebrating on June 17, 2041, when Metropolitan would reach the awesome milestone of 100 years of water delivery to Southern California.

The events and history that will be commemorated in another half century are still evolving and much remains to be accomplished. It is somewhat ironic that, despite the vision of the Southland's water leaders and the vast works they have created, Southern California's future water supply is still far from secure. The facts are irrefutable: Metropolitan's Colorado River supply has been reduced by almost 60 percent; the city of Los Angeles' aqueduct system from the Eastern Sierra Nevada is shackled by environmental and legal restraints; and the State Water Project remains incomplete, lacking the capacity for delivering the total supplies for which it has contracted, much of that water for the Southland.

NO MATTER HOW THEY STRAINED THEIR EYES, NONE COULD SEE AN UNFALTERING LIGHT AT THE END OF THE DROUGHT TUNNEL.

MANY POLITICAL LEADERS SHY AWAY FROM THE TOPIC OF WATER AT PRECISELY THE TIME WHEN COURAGEOUS LEADERSHIP IS DESPERATELY REQUIRED.

Can the Southland's economy survive without a dependable water supply?

But Southern California is not suffering these problems alone. The water supply of virtually every urban area in the state is not as firm as it once was thought to be. Even agriculture, which uses more than 80 percent of the developed water in California, is plagued by shortages in times of drought, as well as by such persistent water problems as salinity and over-drafting of groundwater supplies.

Yet since the early 1970s, when the first phase of the State Water Project was completed, Californians have split over the issue of water. The divisiveness of the 1950s and early '60s appeared to heal as that huge system was constructed, only to return in a newer, more virulent form. The North is still pitted against the South, and to some degree, urban water users against agricultural interests and environmentalists against water agencies. Water has become such a volatile issue that, fearful of alienating huge blocks of voters, many political leaders shy away from the topic at precisely the time when courageous leadership is desperately required.

If California is to continue on the course that has propelled it into a position of prominence and leadership, it has to shake off the decade and a half of procrastination on water matters that has replaced decision-making. There is much to be discussed and accomplished. In Southern California, Metropolitan remains committed to its founding charge of providing supplemental water to Southlanders — today numbering more than 15 million — in a region now extending into six counties. To achieve this, the district has invested $3 billion in an aqueduct and distribution system that permits remarkable operational flexibility. And it is considering doubling that investment to assure Southern California's water future.

Occasionally, Metropolitan has been criticized for being too well-prepared and for overbuilding. In fact, it has constructed a system based on certain worst-case scenarios — extended droughts or earthquakes that would interrupt aqueduct operations. And these very qualities have paid high dividends. During the 1976-77 drought, for example, the district had the flexibility of drawing off the water from one of two aqueducts. So, with 4 million fewer people to serve than today, it gave up much of its allotment of water from the state project, freeing it for use by more needy agencies, while it relied on more water from the Colorado River.

But even this kind of insurance has its limits. Metropolitan pushed its system hard in 1990, the fourth straight year of drought, operating at more than 90 percent of capacity year round and at near-capacity during times of peak demand. With yet another 4 million-plus people projected to be living in its service area by 2010 and water quality standards continuing to become more stringent, Metropolitan once more finds it necessary to expand its treatment and distribution systems. It has begun implementation of elements of a 1988 study that recommended a $3 billion package of projects, a figure that as 1991 unfolded was approaching $6 billion. It is anticipated that work on many of these projects will be launched and completed before the turn of the century. The key elements call for creating a new storage reservoir in Riverside County, constructing major pipelines to carry water to the areas where it will be needed in future decades, building new water treatment plants and expanding existing ones, and implementing a new water treatment process at all of these facilities.

The largest of these projects will be the construction of the new reservoir and the Inland Feeder, a major pipeline that will connect the East Branch of the State Water Project's California Aqueduct with Lake Mathews, the

Domenigoni Valley (in background), site of planned eastside reservoir

terminal reservoir of Metropolitan's Colorado River Aqueduct system located in Riverside County. The impetus to move ahead with the new reservoir was born out of a conversation General Manager Carl Boronkay had with long-time chief planner Donald Brooks while returning from a tour of several district facilities. The Peripheral Canal, which would have been the long-awaited delta transfer facility of the State Water Project, had just gone down to defeat at the polls. Boronkay asked what would be the most important project for the district to next consider in light of the canal's rejection. Without hesitation, Brooks answered, "Additional storage capacity within the district's service area."

Housing in the Inland Empire, fastest growing region in Metropolitan's service area

A study was initiated of potential sites for a reservoir with storage capacity of as much as 1.2 million acre-feet, a figure derived from the district's ongoing system overview study. Some 13 sites in Riverside County received careful consideration, and eventually only three remained — in or near the Domenigoni Valley, Potrero Creek and Vail Lake. The estimated cost of developing one of these sites was approximately $1 billion. Property acquisition proceeded on two of the sites to preserve them from the pressure of residential development until such time as final determinations could be made. The Domenigoni site was subsequently selected by Metropolitan's board. Realization of such a storage facility will contribute mightily to Southern California's water security.

The proposed $700 million Inland Feeder will give Metropolitan added flexibility in operating its system and in storing water for emergency and future use. To keep pace with population growth and expected new water quality standards, a major investment in treatment capacity also will be required. To meet this objective, Metropolitan has under review plans to build two new treatment plants in Riverside County, expand the capacity of its five existing plants and implement a new water treatment technology to meet revised Environmental Protection Agency regulations for trihalomethanes and other contaminants.

THERE MUST BE A REALIZATION THAT MANY WATER ISSUES TRANSCEND LOCAL OR REGIONAL BOUNDARIES AND TRADITIONAL, IF ARBITRARY, INTERESTS.

Though Metropolitan's contemplated $6 billion expansion program is very important, it addresses only one element of a complex problem that must be solved if Southern California is to have sufficient water in the 21st century. Expanding a distribution system is one thing, but additional sources of water must be secured for residential, municipal and industrial uses throughout all of California. And it must be accomplished soon.

Metropolitan will continue to explore the course it pioneered in the 1980s of developing innovative and alternative methods of acquiring new water. The historic conservation agreement between Metropolitan and the Imperial Irrigation District, along with a variety of groundwater storage and banking agreements, will stretch and better utilize existing water resources. Ongoing programs that encourage water conservation and reclamation achieve the same purpose, and additional efforts in these areas will be sought. Someday, even desalination may play a role in augmenting MWD's water supply. Another important component of the mix that will constitute the Southland's water future is water marketing — the voluntary sale of water used presently for agricultural purposes to urban suppliers. Though long talked about, it has been very controversial and, therefore, slow to develop.

As creative and promising as these efforts are, they too are only part of the solution. All of these ideas must be unified into a comprehensive blueprint for meeting future water needs. There must be a realization that many water issues transcend local or regional boundaries and traditional, if arbitrary, interests.

Certainly, this is true of the Sacramento-San Joaquin Delta. This spongy, triangular-shaped sliver of real estate lies at the core of California's water destiny. There can be no state master plan for water that does not resolve problems in the delta. Nearly 150 years of human effort have transformed the region, creating a complex web of interrelated problems that affect water users all across California. Issues of water quality in the delta and in

What does the future hold?

the water it exports, fisheries protection, seismicity and levee restoration cannot be debated endlessly. Rational, balanced decisions must be made, choices that preserve the unique character of the delta while providing for the some 40 percent of all Californians who rely on the area for some or all of their drinking water.

So, too, the impasse over the State Water Project must be brought to a satisfactory conclusion. Designed with bold vision to serve Californians well into the future, the SWP is a truncated version of what it was conceived to be, having the ability to deliver little more than half of the 4.23 million acre-feet of water contracted to be delivered each year in the next century. This condition can be corrected only through the spirit of compromise and consensus of all interest groups.

This history has been one of men and women inspired by the immense task of anticipating Southern California's future and contributing the most critical element to that future. It is one that displays the vision, courage and resourcefulness that were provided time and again in overcoming obstacles to the goal of achieving water security. The Metropolitan Water District of Southern California is, indeed, fortunate in having the example of so many in looking to the challenges it faces.

LEADING THE WAY:
CHAIRMEN OF THE BOARD

The chairman of the board's office at Metropolitan Water District headquarters in downtown Los Angeles is the hub of board activity. Ten Southern California leaders have occupied that office since the district's inception in December of 1928. Though their backgrounds are diverse, all have demonstrated a strong dedication to the cause of assuring a reliable water supply for Southland residents.

W.P. Whitsett

The first board chairman, W. P. Whitsett, longtime banker and land developer who founded the town of Van Nuys and whose early activities had been in coal and mining, was one of the then seven representatives of the city of Los Angeles. As a tribute to his involvement in its development, his name was given to the Whitsett Intake Pumping Plant at Lake Havasu, where Colorado River water starts its journey to the coastal region. He had been a four-year member of the Los Angeles Department of Water and Power board of commissioners when he joined the newly formed Metropolitan board and was made its chairman; he continued two additional years as a commissioner before confining his water activities to the district. As the result of eight unanimous reelections, he filled the office of chairman for nearly 18 years.

Victor Rosetti

The second chairman, Victor Rosetti, again of Los Angeles, assumed the office in January of 1947, Rosetti kept the board reins firmly in the hands of a banker. President of the Farmers and Merchants National Bank, he was one of Southern California's foremost financial and civic leaders. The Southern Pacific Company, Pacific Mutual Life Insurance Company, Mascot Oil Company, Alamitos Land Company and Pacific Telephone and Telegraph all benefitted from his services on their boards. But Rosetti's occupancy of the chairman's office was not to be long-term. A year and a half into his term, he resigned from the board, ending his 15-year affiliation with the district.

John H. Ramboz, of San Marino, also a 15-year member of the board, was named to fill out the remaining six months of Rosetti's term. The new chairman's background also was financial, having been connected for 25 years with the Merchants National Bank of Los Angeles before becoming a financial counsellor to several large corporations and a director of the J. W. Robinson Company. Thus, from its inception, the man at the helm of the Metropolitan board had come from the world of finance.

John H. Ramboz

A strong-willed, highly respected representative of the city of Los Angeles, Joseph Jensen, not only was to break that mold, he was to become legend at Metropolitan. He became the board's fourth chairman in 1949 and served until his death in 1974, with 25 years, the district's longest tenured in the office. Geology and mining engineering were his early fields; however, the major thrust of his career was fine-tuned to oil. He joined the Tidewater Oil Company and, though the name had changed to Getty in the interim, he spent the next 38 years there, rising to become assistant to the western general manager prior to his 1955 retirement. Many years of consulting — both with Getty and with Southern Pacific — followed. Like Whitsett, Jensen also served on the Los Angeles Department of Water and Power board of commissioners — in his case, a four-year term. Jensen's years as Metropolitan chairman saw the district go from 16 member agencies serving some 3.5 million people to 27 serving nearly three times as many. He guided the board through intensive periods of conflict over water rights on the Colorado River; the years of major expansion of Metropolitan's aqueduct from that river; through the politically sensitive days of determining to go with the State Water Project, a course which he initially adamantly opposed; and then through the major distribution system expansion necessary to carry northern water to Southland consumers. Jensen held tight to the reins of influence and power at Metropolitan. Though a relatively small man in stature, he was larger than life; he reportedly would go to Sacramento on business relating to the proposed state project and, without an appointment, walk past the governor's secretary and into the office with no challenge given. Congressman James C. Corman, in paying him tribute, noted, "I have

Joseph Jensen

known and feared Joe Jensen for some 20 years.... For his size, he is an awesome figure... tough, thoughtful and dedicated."

Warren Butler

At the time of Jensen's death in 1974, the longest-serving board member and then 25-year vice chairman, Warren Butler, who represented the city of Compton, was named to fill the remaining five months of Jensen's term. And this he did with the same quiet assurance with which he had approached his commitment to Metropolitan made nearly 40 years before. He was appointed to the board as Compton's representative just six years after accepting the city editor post on the Compton News Tribune and only one year before he would step into the editor's shoes of what later would be known as the Herald-American newspapers in southern Los Angeles County. Following an incident in which "a street department repairman stuck a pick into a water pipe and the whole town was out of water in 20 minutes," with the consent of his publisher, he ran a continuing campaign for Compton to build itself a good water distribution system. It took 20 years, but he was successful. He retired from the newspaper business — with the exception of continuing to write a column for the chain — in 1957, and devoted even more of his time to water matters. He retired from the Metropolitan board in 1980, and his record of 45 years of dedication stands today.

Butler had made it clear upon accepting the chairmanship that he was interested only in filling out Jensen's term. During that brief time, term limitations for officers were enacted by Metropolitan's board — a maximum of two two-year terms — and the structure of the board's officers was altered to provide for three vice chairmen rather than one. Times were changing; water was becoming more politicized and the issues more complicated.

The first to serve as chairman in the new era was Howard H. Hawkins of Upper San Gabriel Valley Municipal Water District. A businessman — at that time vice president and general manager of the Golden State Plant

Howard H. Hawkins

Earle C. Blais

Food company in Glendora — and former mayor of Covina, Hawkins had joined the Metropolitan board in 1963. In accepting the gavel in January of 1975, he saw construction of the Peripheral Canal as the district's number one priority, while recognizing other important issues to include the cost of energy and its availability to pump water supplies, a situation that would place burdens on the pricing of water. Before the end of his four years in the chairman's office, he would lead the board through the first major drought since Metropolitan's inception. Hawkins brought to the chairmanship a background rich in civic government and community affairs. Following his tenure as chairman, Hawkins continued to serve on the Metropolitan board through the end of 1989. Throughout his MWD career, Hawkins was active in a variety of water organizations, serving as Metropolitan's representative on the Colorado River Board and as president of the Association of California Water Agencies and of the Colorado River Water Users Association.

Attorney and former Burbank mayor Earle C. Blais accepted the responsibilities of board chairman in January 1979. A tall man with a deep voice, he cast an imposing figure in the ensuing four years, as he traveled the state to spread the message of the need for the Peripheral Canal — first in support of SB 200 as it made its way through the Legislature and later to explain Metropolitan's position once a referendum put the measure on the June 1982 ballot as Proposition 9. No stranger to civic activities, Blais had been active in Burbank politics since the early 1950s, and had been named that city's Citizen of the Year in 1961, the same year the council named him to the Metropolitan board. During his four years as chairman he devoted more time to water issues than he did to his own law practice. When he stepped down as chairman, he noted, "My biggest disappointment was the inability of the water community to convince Southern Californians of the seriousness of the water problems we face. There is no doubt in my mind we are in a precarious position."

"It will be a hard job to fill the shoes of Earle Blais, but I'm going to try," announced E. Thornton Ibbetson, as he picked up the gavel to become the new chairman in 1983. And, lest there be doubt, he confirmed that his first priority was "to work with water leaders statewide to complete the State Water Project." Ibbetson, representing Central Basin Municipal Water District, had joined the MWD board in 1959, and had served the preceding four years as its secretary. The Ibbetson name was well-known in southeastern Los Angeles County due to the family's substantial business and civic contributions to the area where his father had founded the family business in 1895. Though that business, Union Development Company, and Ibbetson-Marsh Realtors were Ibbetson's current major involvements, his background included a lengthy list of other activities: farming, construction, real estate, operating various commercial enterprises, negotiating geothermal energy leases. For awhile, he even ran a small water company. He would lead the board in setting policy for four years that were to become a period of innovation at Metropolitan.

E. Thornton Ibbetson

With the election of E. L. Balmer to succeed Ibbetson in 1987, support for innovative water programs continued. Large in stature, he was a no-nonsense man of few unnecessary words who had a strong commitment to Southern California and the development of dependable water supplies. He was appointed to the Metropolitan board in 1976 as one of the representatives of West Basin Municipal Water District. Employed at that time by Standard Oil at its El Segundo refinery, he would retire in 1980 as superintendent of the asphalt, utilities and plant security division, having been with the company for 41 years. During World War II, he had served in the U.S. Army Transportation Corps, attaining the rank of major before his discharge in 1946; he had remained in the Army Reserves until 1966. Active in civic affairs, Balmer was elected to the El Segundo City Council in 1968 and served as mayor before leaving the council in 1980. As board chairman, Balmer became a familiar face throughout water circles state- and nationwide, eager to keep informed about all aspects of water supply. Balmer was in the first year of his second term at the time of his death in May 1989.

E.L. Balmer

Lois B. Krieger

Following Balmer's death, for the first time in the district's 60-year-plus history, a woman was elected to the office of chairman of the board. Chosen to fill the unexpired term, Lois B. Krieger would subsequently be elected to a full term to begin in January 1991. Krieger, a longtime participant in Southern California water matters, joined the Metropolitan board in 1976 as the representative of the Western Municipal Water District of Riverside County. She was only the second director to represent that district, the first having been her father, Howard Boylan, who served in that capacity for nearly 22 years. Active in water organizations statewide, she is a past president of the Association of California Water Agencies and a member of the boards of directors of the Water Education Foundation and the California Water Resources Association. At the onset of 1991, Mrs. Krieger found Metropolitan in the midst of the most severe drought with which any previous board has had to deal. However, the actions of her administration are focused beyond the current drought, however serious. "I think our challenge," she declares, "and the challenge of all Southern Californians, is to reach for the same degree of water dependability as did those who envisioned the Colorado River Aqueduct."

CARRYING OUT THE MISSION:
PROFILES IN MANAGEMENT

The general manager of the Metropolitan Water District of Southern California has no spare time on his hands. And that's the way it has been since the beginning. It is true that the emphasis of the organization has shifted considerably over the nearly 63 years since its inception from one enormous responsibility to another. Running Metropolitan has evolved from a primary goal of building a system to provide a water supply for some 1.7 million Southlanders in 13 cities in Los Angeles and Orange counties to a primary goal of managing a system to ensure a sufficient water supply for an area that is home to more than 15 million people, an area now covering 5,200 square miles in six Southern California counties. That water supply must sustain not only the multiplying millions of residents, but one of the world's most robust economies. This has, of necessity, required an evolving set of qualifications in Metropolitan's general managers, taking the major requirement from that of being a top-notch engineer to that of a being a manager whose skills are more people oriented, a person whose forte is effectiveness in a social/political/economic milieu.

F.E. Weymouth

Nine men of various talents have filled this job.

F. E. Weymouth took the reins as Metropolitan's first chief engineer in 1929 — general manager would be added to his title three years later. A highly respected builder of dams who came out of the Bureau of Reclamation, his credits included supervision of the building of the storage dam on the Snake River at Jackson Lake, Wyoming, and the Arrowrock Dam on the Boise River in Idaho, at 349 feet, the highest in the world at the time of its construction. During his subsequent stint as chief engineer of the bureau, the organization pioneered the development of new methods of dam design and building which would be proved successful some years later by what would be called Hoover Dam, majestically standing at more than twice the height of Arrowrock. Weymouth would see Metropolitan through the construction of the Colorado River Aqueduct and MWD's initial distribution system. And just five weeks after that system was put into operation, he suffered a fatal heart attack in his home in San Marino. The reins of leadership were turned over to the man who had been his assistant chief engineer throughout his near 13 years with the district. History would record that a remarkable job had been done, for 14 years later in 1955, the Colorado River Aqueduct was selected by the American Society of Civil Engineers as one of the seven modern civil engineering wonders of the United States.

Julian B. Hinds

Julian B. Hinds — who in a mid-1970s interview said, "I got my feet wet in 1910, and they haven't been dry since" — by his own count had 31 years in engineering when he accepted those reins. He remembered when concrete was a new material. He sought out challenges of his designs from other engineers to help assure that his work would stand the test of many minds. He brought to Metropolitan experience on more than 120 dams in the United States and Mexico. And after leaving the district, he did consultant work on some 60 more. It was while working in Mexico that he became acquainted with Frank Weymouth. As a result, in 1929 Weymouth offered him two choices: to do the preliminary design of the Colorado River Aqueduct or the detailed design and construction of the 700-foot-high Hoover Dam, but not both. Hinds, who said he "really wanted to be twins" chose the aqueduct. In bowing out 10 years after becoming general manager and chief engineer of Metropolitan Water District, Hinds, many felt, may never have received the acclaim he really deserved as he was always at least one or two steps ahead of the accolades. However, bow out he did because he was 70 years old and at that time 70 was mandatory retirement age.

Robert B. Diemer

Robert B. Diemer was next to step into the shoes of general manager and chief engineer. With an extensive engineering career in construction of canals and dams dating back to 1911, Diemer too was an alumnus of the Bureau of Reclamation, charting 15 years in the construction of irrigation projects in Nebraska and Wyoming. As had Hinds, Diemer had been brought to Metropolitan in 1929 by Weymouth whom he had met while developing irrigation works in Mexico. A man totally dedicated to his work, no detail was too small for Diemer's attention. It was often claimed that he not only wrote the letters, but licked the stamps as well. One heavy duty equipment operator at a desert pumping plant remembered Diemer as having "a loud roar that he used generously and a heart just as big, though he'd give you hell for recognizing that." He knew the aqueduct system like the palm of his hand, and in his nine years as the district's chief administrative officer, Diemer directed the $220 million expansion program that brought the Colorado River Aqueduct to its full delivery capacity of 1 billion gallons a day. He retired December 31, 1961, and at the January 1962 board meeting, he was seated as the representative of the city of Pasadena, a position he would fill for almost five years.

Robert A. Skinner

MWD's next general manager, Robert A. Skinner, who had joined Metropolitan in 1933, has been described by colleagues as "an engineer who was one of the best lawyers the district ever had" though he had no legal training, as "a man who had an unusual respect for the English language and used it with exactness and grace," and as someone who was "meticulous and painstaking, who would examine the meaning of every sentence written in Metropolitan documents and wanted everything as accurate and precise as possible." It was three years into Skinner's tenure in the leadership position that the responsiblities of the chief engineer were separated from those of the general manager. A big job was under way — the $3 billion expansion of Metropolitan's distribution system to handle the water coming from Northern California. Yet Skinner long remembered his most exciting assignment with the district to have been before he became GM — the year-long "pressing activity of the negotiations of Metropolitan's contract with the state [for state project water]. . . . The last weeks were very high pressure. Telegrams were flying back and forth between our board and the governor's office. I often wondered if the successful negotiation of the contract was instrumental in the successful vote."

Henry J. Mills

Frank M. Clinton

On March 1, 1967, Henry J. "Hank" Mills became the first general manager who had started out as a worker on a survey party; by the time he would retire some four and a half years later, he would be wrapping up a 41-year career with Metropolitan. Mills was a popular choice with district employees. He was one of their own — a genial man who could call a great many by their first names, an aqueduct builder who had walked the same ground they now walked. He had spent his early years on the desert moving from site to site, taking on a variety of responsibilities: supervision and inspection of tunnel construction, resident engineer of Mecca Pass and Cottonwood tunnels, the concrete lining of several distribution system tunnels. Upon completion of the aqueduct system, Metropolitan began to grow, and Mills' career grew right with it — right up to assistant chief engineer, and when the title chief engineer was split from that of general manager, he moved into that spot. Mills recalled that when be became general manager in 1967, "there was again an aqueduct being built — only this time it was the State Water Project." However, Metropolitan's involvement wasn't in actual construction of the facilities. Rather, there were endless strings of meetings — mostly in Sacramento. And there was the expansion of Metropolitan's distribution system to be completed. The evolution of the general manager's position was continuing.

In late 1971, Frank M. Clinton succeeded Mills as general manager. He had joined Metropolitan in 1965 as chief project engineer after retiring as a regional director from the U.S. Bureau of Reclamation where he had spent 28 years. In his new position at Metropolitan, he would be responsible for preparing economic, manpower and construction studies and schedules for the district's $1.3 billion expansion program. Named general manager in 1971, Clinton would occupy that office less time than anyone prior or since — only two and a half years. But they were two and a half eventful years. The district's service area was now home to more than 10 million people, and during Clinton's tenure, Metropolitan would put the final touches on the expansion of the distribution system and would receive its first deliveries of water through the State Water Project — at Castaic Lake on the California Aqueduct's West Branch in 1972 and at Lake Perris on its East Branch the following spring. But, though planned since the mid-1960s, a major portion of the project was yet to be built. As he readied himself for retirement, Clinton readied Metropolitan to marshal its energies toward construction of the identified transdelta facility — the Peripheral Canal.

When Clinton retired, the first non-engineer to occupy the general manager position was named, then Metropolitan general counsel, John Lauten. A believer in planning for the worst in order to make the best of whatever happened, Lauten carried that philosophy into his responsibilities as general manager. He learned that approach, he said, in large part from his months in combat in World War II with one of the most celebrated fighting divisions in U.S. Army history, the Big Red One; the multi-decorated Lauten emerged from the army a colonel. His career following the war took him from assistant city attorney in Glendale to city attorney in Fresno and then back to Southern California in 1963 to become Metropolitan's assistant general counsel and subsequently general counsel. In stepping into the position of general manager on May 1, 1974, the no-nonsense Lauten, recognizing the change in direction of the district, felt the need to streamline management approaches. In addition to moving the Peripheral Canal along if the needs of the future were to be met, he saw a growing importance and difficulty in maintaining and improving water quality and in the conservation and reclamation of water supplies. And he had the immediate task of dealing with the drastic changes in the cost and availability of energy.

John Lauten

Evan L. Griffith had packed his first lieutenant bars away and joined MWD as a junior engineer in 1952, after having served 15 months in Korea as a platoon commander with the U.S. Marine Corps. Twenty-five years later, upon being selected MWD general manager, he noted, "In the old days, the general manager was involved in every aspect of the district and all decisions were made by him. I don't work that way." A colleague explained, "He expected us to perform and to keep him informed." Another said, "He put a lot of faith in his people. He gave you authority, gave you backing, but always kept an eye on you, even bailed you out when you needed it." A large, relaxed man, with a marvelous sense of humor, Griff's first love at Metropolitan was construction; he was chief construction engineer in the late 1960s when the distribution system was expanded to take water from the state project, supervising the building of more than 300 miles of pipelines, tunnels and facilities. In 1974, he was named assistant chief engineer in charge of construction and the following year, assistant general manager. And in 1977, this man who believes "listening is the key to being responsive" and built a reputation on his ability to listen, became general manager.

Evan L. Griffith

The next and current general manager of Metropolitan has been described as "the consummate public servant... thoroughly knowledgeable of and completely dedicated to his work." Carl Boronkay became general manager in March of 1984, the second attorney to serve in this demanding position. A cultured man, a voracious reader, a fellow with a strong sense of humor and an optimistic attitude toward life, Boronkay is a job-oriented man concerned about everyone doing the best job possible for the district. In 1976, he came to Metropolitan from the California Attorney General's office, where he had been senior assistant attorney general, heading the public resources group, to serve as the district's assistant general counsel. He was observed as being a litigator who really loved the intellectual challenge of getting on his feet and debating others. In 1980, Boronkay became the district's general counsel and in that capacity experienced the high point of his legal career: arguing before the U.S. Supreme Court — and winning. While promoting various innovative programs to augment Southern California's water supplies, he takes special interest in the heralded water conservation program with the Imperial Irrigation District and needed progress on the

Carl Boronkay

State Water Project. In connection with the latter, he has been described in an adversary's testimony prepared for a Congressional hearing as waging a "lonely but spirited" fight for the Peripheral Canal. Not reluctant to take on controversial issues, he has strongly supported water transfers through marketing as an essential component of the Southland's future water supply.

REFLECTIONS OF LONGTIME BOARD MEMBERS

THOUGHTS AND OPINIONS OF FIVE WHO HAVE 20 YEARS OR MORE SERVICE

E. Thornton Ibbetson pauses a moment in remembering his first days on the board 32 years earlier when he was appointed as one of five representatives of Central Basin Municipal Water District to the Metropolitan Water District. The board totaled 37 members representing 24 member agencies. Metropolitan was just completing the expansion of the Colorado River Aqueduct and looking to the needs of the future as it planned for the State Water Project.

E. Thornton Ibbetson

"Our board meetings went from 10 o'clock in the morning until 5 o'clock at night. There were a lot of things to consider in formulating the state contracts — from the wording to our electing to pay up front rather than pay-as-you-go. Once we made the determination to go with the State Water Project, it was down to the long, hard negotiations — very, very technical, very, very tough.

"In those days, Dairy Valley had cows and Orange County had trees," he continues, noting that today Central Basin is 95 percent urbanized. "Things were tremendously different then. We were trying to sell water. We were only selling about 60 percent of our Colorado River Aqueduct supply. San Diego was our biggest user and we were very grateful to them. They were the ones who were paying our bills. We didn't have the controversy about new annexations then that we have now. We were looking for annexations in those days, trying to close all the "windows" in our service area that we could. It's different today. Almost all our efforts are directed at saving water."

As 1990 drew to a close, Ibbetson, who had served as chairman from January 1983 to January 1987, was one of only two members of MWD's board of directors whose service topped the 30-year mark, one of only five who had 20 years under their belts. Lynndon L. Aufdenkamp, one of two representatives of the Coastal Municipal Water District, by that time had served on the Metropolitan board almost 34 years, and had been the sole representative of his district for some 20 of those years. Harry Griffen, one of six representatives of the San Diego County Water Authority, and Charles D. Barker, one of West Basin Municipal Water District's three representatives, had both become members in 1963. Carl E. Ward, one of two who today represent Calleguas Municipal Water District in Ventura County, came on board in 1969 and 11 years passed before Calleguas qualified for a second representative.

All five longtime Metropolitan directors find the issues with which the board had to deal early in their tenures and the issues with which it must deal today to be of equal magnitude. All five also feel that dealing with the issues today is very different than in years past.

"I don't believe the challenges to the district that I faced as a new director were much different than the challenges of today: growth and the need to meet increasing water demands," recalls Aufdenkamp. "Playing a part in the development of the State Water Project was a happy experience and most rewarding. The board, it seems to me, has never been closer, or as close, to state legislators, the governor and other statewide officials, as it was during that time. The political scene is more complex and difficult today."

Lynndon L. Aufdenkamp

"Issues were just as varied then as now," Ibbetson agrees. "However, everything seemed to go then. Today we are trying to find ways to conserve, trying to find places to store water underground, trying to find water transfer situations like the Imperial Valley where we can put in conservation measures in exchange for the water conserved. These things are going on and these things do provide challenges. But when it comes to the big things we need to do today, new water projects, there are roadblocks. Every time we turn around, the north has us roadblocked, the Legislature has us roadblocked because they all have to worry about getting re-elected or somebody is trying to tie our purse strings. It's very frustrating."

Barker, too, believes that Metropolitan is finding it harder and harder to

Charles D. Barker

accomplish what it needs to accomplish. "It seems you cannot build anything today that we built in the past — and if we hadn't, then where would we be?" he queries. "Seeing something completed, seeing it meet the water requirements, was truly satisfying. You try something today and you lose. So you Mickey Mouse it — which is what we're doing instead of building the Peripheral Canal."

Just about the time Barker and Griffen joined the Metropolitan board, the Peripheral Canal was being designated as the transdelta facility for the State Water Project. "We didn't worry much about it in those days because we knew it was going to be built," recalls Griffen. "All kinds of plans for the delta had been thoroughly studied; task forces had worked to come up with the best plan." And the canal was selected. Since that time, it has repeatedly undergone further study, legislative action and, finally, a referendum to block its construction. "I think the delta is the most thoroughly studied thing in the world," concludes Griffen. Yet the solution for completing the State Water Project is yet to be agreed upon.

Ward had been appointed to the Metropolitan board 17 years after he first became interested in water issues. In 1952, he had run for the Oxnard City Council on the platform of doing something about the quality of the water being pumped in the city. Throughout the rest of that decade, he worked to join forces with interests in the eastern part of Ventura County to form the Calleguas Municipal Water District and join Metropolitan, which took place in 1960. Ward was appointed to Metropolitan's board to replace Calleguas' first representative who had served for eight years. He reached Metropolitan just three years before the first water arrived from the State Water Project; the issue of the day was completion of the distribution system to handle the northern supplies. "There weren't the same types of problems that are hitting us in the face now, coming from all directions," he says. "There was no thought of limiting growth by limiting water supply. There were no environmental issues. The Peripheral Canal was the first big thing that Calleguas got into as a member agency of Metropolitan. And that's when things became so political."

When Barker joined the MWD board representing West Basin, he had nearly a dozen years on his local board behind him, and he had spent considerable time in 1960 "beating the bushes" to obtain passage of Proposition 1, providing authorization of the State Water Project. His company, Standard Oil of California, had dedicated his time to that effort. Seawater intrusion had been of great concern to his agency; it was an issue that he knew had to be addressed. The water quality debates of the day were on the organics problems of state water versus the minerals problems of Colorado River water, rather than today's emphasis on the increasingly tough drinking water quality standards being set by the Environmental Protection Agency. "Industry was a major player in the West Basin Water Association," he points out. "They knew how important water quality was to their operations. With poor water, their treatment expenses could double and triple. I found that on the MWD board in those days the differences among members were primarily about engineering things, such as whether there should be a single- or multi-stage pump lift. We always had public support for projects; today it's all political."

ILLUSTRATING CURRENT QUESTIONING OF LONG-ESTABLISHED BOARD POLICY IS THE ISSUE OF ANNEXATIONS.

Illustrating current questioning of long-established board policy is the issue of annexations. "When Calleguas annexed to Metropolitan in 1960," Ward remembers, "it was just assumed that as agriculture phased out in Ventura County, there would be development and the entire Oxnard plain would eventually be annexed to the district. That was before growth popped up as an issue; now, I think it won't be for many more years."

Barker recalls that initially it was understood that Metropolitan was expected to "fill in" the district, that just about all urban areas in Southern California would be annexed. "That is, until the 1977 drought," he clarifies. "That's the first time the policy of annexations came under question.

Politics is a word that seems to crop up over and over again in discussions of water supply in the 1990s.

At that time we called a moratorium." And there have been other moratoriums for varied reasons since. The annexation controversy on today's board has developed and been debated as future water supplies have become less certain.

Aufdenkamp comments that having a pro-annexation policy is not to say that there hasn't always been very close scrutiny of individual annexations. "The concerns at the time, however, were not fixed on the idea that the district would run out of water, but rather, were there windows?...Could adjacent lands, not annexed, get a free ride by pumping from the same basin?...Or could they be unjustly enriched by increased land values?... What was the purpose of the service?...Would service to existing members be impaired? Some requests were sent back for revision of boundaries or closing of windows."

Griffen points out that annexations raised other concerns. "In the '50s, San Diego County Water Authority worried that we only had a right to so much Colorado River water and if just the land that was already in the district was developed, there might not be enough. So we went to the water problems committee and asked that it furnish the water authority with a statement that there was sufficient water to take care of the full development of the lands already in the district. There was about two months of deliberation, but out of that came the Laguna Declaration, which took care of San Diego's concerns. It wasn't debated much, because it said what everybody wanted it to say."

Politics is a word that seems to crop up over and over again in discussions of water supply in the 1990s. "I wish that our reservoirs were as full of water as our water is full of politics," observes Aufdenkamp. "Water issues have been used and abused by politicians with increasing frequency. I think the only way this can be overcome is to find a way to make water a people issue. Let them pressure their elected representatives in Sacramento. We must learn the game and play it better than the politicians do."

Ward agrees that times have changed, the public has changed and even the way the board of directors reacts to the public has changed. "The demands for water must be met," he says. "There's no alternative to that. So I guess it's going to have to be worked out politically. I think our conservation efforts have made people more cognizant of the need for water than they were before. Perhaps that will help."

Harry Griffen

Considering the part politics play in water supply, Griffen says, "The people have to bring the pressure on the politicians. Not Metropolitan, but the people. All politicians worry about getting reelected. We need grass roots participation. That's how we get to the Legislature."

The casual observer might assume that similar political influences would be a factor in the internal activities of Metropolitan board members. Just how big a problem is it for any board member to vote the best interests of his or her appointing agency versus the best interests of Metropolitan as a whole?

Ibbetson believes things are better for the smaller agencies than they have been in a long time. "With the local projects and conservation credits programs, they are really coming alive. They are in a much better position to be able to do things for their constituents than they have been in the past."

Barker believes no conflict exists; he feels representing West Basin is representing Metropolitan. "What we're spending today is primarily to provide water for the developing areas just as we provided yesterday for the areas which are pretty secure today. Los Angeles, Central Basin, Pasadena, West Basin — we're all mature areas. I don't think it's the Metropolitan spirit to suddenly take the attitude that if it's their county, they should be paying for it. One thing that concerns me if I see it on a board such as ours is block voting. I think when you have lost honest disagreement, you have lost the expertise of a lot of people. When you are told how to vote you become a puppet."

Griffen strongly agrees. "I've always taken the position, you appoint me and then I'm on my own. Each member should have that freedom, even an agency like mine where there are six different people representing the same interests. If there should be occasions where we might differ in opinion, that's just a split vote. And I don't see anything wrong with a split vote."

In contemplating the changes on the board since his first meeting in January of 1957, Aufdenkamp notes, "It has been said that after 30 years the pendulum swings and it is the end of an era. I believe that is certainly so with the Metropolitan board. There's been a change in board membership, with consequent loss of institutional memory; a change in the standards by which the experience of potential appointees are judged by some appointing authorities; a changing concept of the district's mission and the long-established policies designed to achieve that mission. There seems to be a change in attitude."

Carl E. Ward

Recalling his first board meeting, he continues, "I was awe-struck by the distinguished 36 business and professional leaders that quietly filled the small board room atop Sid Graumann's Million Dollar Theatre building at 3rd and Broadway in downtown Los Angeles. It was like entering a courtroom. The power of the chair permeated the room. Joe Jensen ran a tight ship. Fortunately, a director's inspection tour had been scheduled for the following week. This provided onsite information about issues facing the board. And it provided the opportunity to get better acquainted with my colleagues and to examine together, on an informal basis, the problems facing the district. These field trips are as vital to the director's role as doing the homework that is required before a board meeting."

Griffen, too, believes that there has been a considerable change in the board's composition, the most notable difference being in the ages of its members. He remembers the group when he came on board, "Many retired, many semiretired, they were primarily seasoned executives, professionals and civic leaders. They had achieved career levels that permitted a considerable portion of their time and interests to be devoted to the affairs of Metropolitan. There was a marked effort to formulate policy that enabled the staff to properly run the district. Today some board members come from families where both the husband and the wife work for a living. They are very busy career people who have limited time available. So they are inclined to devote that time to the subject most closely connected with their career."

Barker compares the district today and yesterday very succinctly: "Sure, the times have changed and along with them, the make-up of the board, and we are doing things differently. But our job is the same — to make sure Southern California has enough water. We can't forget that."

"Our job is the same — to make sure Southern California has enough water. We can't forget that."

— *Barker*

INDEX

A

Alameda County Water District, 134
Alamo Canal, 35, 36
All-American Canal, 38, 84, 94, 167, 168
American River, 93, 105
Anaheim, City of, 43
Annexations by MWD, 43, 84-87, 202, 205-206
Archibald, George, 109
Arizona, 59, 67, 83, 87
Arizona National Guard, 72
"Arizona Navy," 72
Arizona vs. California, 83-84. 119, 128, 160-161, 163
Arvin-Edison Water Storage District, 169-170
Ashley, William, 31
Assembly Bill 1710, 157
Aufdenkamp, Lynndon L., 202, 203, 206, 208-209
Ayala, Senator Ruben, 151, 152, 157

B

Baja California, 9, 45. 172
Balmer, E. L., 193
Banks, Harvey O., 107, 110, 112, 116, 122, 130
Barker, Charles D., 203, 204, 205, 207-208, 209
Bergland, Lt. Eric, 35
Bechtel Corporation report, 107, 109
Beverly Hills, City of, 43
Biermond, Cornelius, 144-145
Black Canyon, site of future Hoover Dam, 34
Blais, Earle C., 152, 191
Bond issues, City of Los Angeles, 17, 18, 19, 46; MWD, 52-55, 88; SWP, 111, 116-118
Bornt, Lester, 166
Boronkay, Carl, 162-166, 185, 200-201
Boswell, J.G. Company, 155, 156
Bottorff, Allen, 115-116
Boulder Canyon Project Act, 40, 41, 58
Boulder Dam 39, 57, 58, 66, 68, 73, 82, (see Hoover Dam)
Brody, Ralph, 110, 131
Brooks, Donald, 185
Brown, Edmund G. "Pat", 103, 109-117, 122, 131, 156
Brown, Edmund G. Jr. "Jerry", 148, 149, 151, 152, 154, 155, 157
Bucket-wheel excavator, 123
Burbank, City of, 43
Bureau of Reclamation, 57, 72, 83, 104-105, 150-151, 168
Burns, Senator Hugh, 111
Burns-Porter Act, 111, 112, 120, 130, 131, 133, 151, 153, 159
Butler, Warren, 191

C

Cabazon Shaft, San Jacinto Tunnel, 69
California Aqueduct, 120, 134, 168, 184; East Branch, 121, 134, 158, 184, 199; West Branch, 121, 134, 199
California Development Company, 36
California Institute of Technology, 76
California, post-WW II period, 78
California Water Plan of 1957, 106, 107, 108, 123
Calleguas Municipal Water District, 87, 203, 204, 205
Canals, 67, 74, 75
Castaic Lake, 121, 134
Central Arizona Project, (CAP), 83, 128, 159, 160
Central Basin Municipal Water District, 87, 202
Central Valley Project, 100-101, 133. 104-105, 151, 169
Chaffey, George, 36
Chino Basin Municipal Water District, 87, 170
Chipps Island, 137
Chiriaco, Joe, 48
Chlorination, 174, 176, 178
Chlorimination, 174, 176, 178
Climate, 78, 92
Clinton, Frank M., 129, 198-199
Coachella Canal, 167-168
Coachella Valley Water District, 162, 166-169
Coastal Municipal Water District, 84, 202
Colorado River, survey and expeditions, 24-25, 32-36; early explorers, 26-31; states contiguous to, 40; acre-foot share of, 81; 82, 128, 141, 168, 169, 174, 180, 181
Colorado River Aqueduct, choosing route, 41; alternate routes, 45, 51; 67, 71, 73; completion of, 76-77; 81, 84-85, 87; expansion of, 88-89; 90, 151, 160, 168, 173, 176, 185
Colorado River Commission, 39
Colorado River Compact, 39-40, 81-83
Colorado River, upper and lower basin states, 38-40
Colton, City of, 43
Compton, City of, 43
Concrete, 20, 22, 74
Contamination of groundwater basins, 161
Contra Costa Canal, 142, 153
Contra Costa County, 156
Coolidge, President Calvin, 42
Cooper, Charles, 113
Copper Basin Reservoir, 76
Costa, Assemblyman Jim, 157, 158
Chowchilla River, 138

D

Decision 1485, 145
Delta (Sacramento-San Joaquin), 100, 105, 120, 122, 130, 134-135, 137; annual inflow, 141; 149, 153, 157, 169; water quality, 140-144, 186; islands in, 139, 204
Department of Fish and Game, 134
Department of Water Resources, 106, 107, 110, 112, 122, 127, 128, 131-134, 141, 149, 150, 162-163, 180
Desalination, 162, 171, 172, 186
Desert Training Center, Gen. George S. Patton, 79
Desert Water Agency, 168, 169
Deukmejian, Governor George, 148, 157, 159
Diemer, Robert, 2, 58-59, 79, 196-197
Dietrich, Noah, 116, 117
Domenigoni Valley, 185
Dowd, Munson, 88
Dry Creek, 138
Drought, of 1862-63, 13; of early 1920s, 24; 86; of 1976-77, 151, 181, 183; of 1986-91, 159, 180-181, 183; emergency water bank, 162; 182
"Duke's Ditch," 157

E

East Bay Municipal Utility District (MUD), 98, 142
East Branch (SWP), 121, 134, 184, 199; expansion of, 158
Eastern Municipal Water District, 87
Eastin, Howard, 124-125
Eaton, Fred, 17-19
Edmonston, Robert, 106, 166
Edmonston, A.D., 103-107, 118, 122, 127, 135
Eel River, 108, 109, 113, 153
El Dorado Canyon, 32
Emergency Relief Funds, 101
Environmental Protection Agency, 146, 174, 176, 178, 185, 205
Environmental Impact Reports, 150-151, 158
Etiwanda Power Plant, 171
Expansion program (CRA), 87-89
Explorers and padres, Southern California and Colorado River history, 7, 9, 28-30, 137-138

F

Fan Hill siphon, 74
Feather River Project, 103-112, 123, 124, 134
Federal Power Commission, 171
Fields, Bud, 61
Finney Resolution, 41

Flint, Senator Frank, 19
Flood of 1861-62, 92; of 1904, 36
Flood control, 82, 92, 93
"Fly camps," survey crews, 46
Foothill Feeder, 129.
Foothill Municipal Water District, 87
Fort Mojave, 32, 35
Fort Yuma, 32
Franciscan priests, 10-11, 25, 91
Fullerton, City of, 43

G

Garfield, Dr. Sidney, 63-64
Garlock earthquake fault, 126
Garvey Reservoir, Monterey Park, 89
Gene, Field Headquarters, 76, 81
Gianelli, William, 133-134
Gila River, 32, 36
Glendale, City of, 43
Gold dredger tailings, 123-124
Gold Rush, 11, 31-32, 93, 123, 138
Goldberg, B. Abbott, 110
Gram, Andrew, 45, 54
Grand Canyon, Arizona, 26, 33-34
Granite Mountains, 75
Granular activated carbon (GAC) process, 178
Great Depression, 46, 54, 59, 62-63
Green, Larry, 76, 80
Green River, 26, and confluence with Grand, 33
Griffen, Harry, 203, 204, 206, 207, 208, 209
Griffith, Evan L., 129, 199-200
Groundwater basins and storage, 86, 161, 168-170

H

Hadley, Eb, 35
Hall, William Hammond, 95-96, 103
Hanson, Chester, 72
Hawkins, Howard H., 191-192
Hayfield pumping plant, 76
Health care, prepaid, 63-64
Heilbron, Fred, 86
Hetch Hetchy, 97-98, 142
Hinds, Julian B., 58, 59, 76, 196
Hitchcock, Secretary of the Interior Ethan, 19
Holburt, Myron, 164
Hoover Dam, 88, 169, (see Boulder Dam)
Hoover, Gainor, 81
Hoover, Secretary of Commerce Herbert, 39
Hospital, desert, 63
House of Representatives, U.S., 19
Huntington Hotel, Pasadena, 43
Hyatt, Edward, 103-104, 106
Hydraulic mining, 94-95, 139
Hydroelectric power plants, 170-171

I

Ibbetson, E. Thornton, 192-193, 202, 203, 207
Imperial Irrigation District, 162-168, 186
Indian tribes, Southern California and Colorado River history, 7-8, 26, 29, 30, 34, 92
Inland Feeder, 184, 185
Interagency Delta Committee, 131
International Boundary and Water Commission, 82
Inyo County agreement, 161
Iron Mountain Pumping Plant, 62, 75, 79
Isleton, California, 140
Ives, Lt. Joseph Christmas, 32-33

J

Jawbone Canyon, 23
Jennings, Bill, 85
Jensen filtration plant, 129
Jensen, Joseph, 108, 112, 113, 115, 116, 117, 190-191
Jesuit priests, "Black Robes," 29
Johnson, George, 32
Johnson, Senator Hiram, 40, 41
"Julia B," ferry boat, 72
Jumbo, heavy equipment, 68

K

Kapiloff, Assemblyman Lawrence, 153
Kennedy, David N., 157, 158
Kennedy, John Fitzgerald, 117, 118
Kern County Water Agency, 116
Kern Water Bank, 158
Kinsey, Don, 52, 54
Klamath River, 105, 153
Knight, Governor Goodwin, 107, 109
Krieger, Lois B., 194

L

Lake Mathews, CRA terminal reservoir, 2, 57, 88-89, 176
Lake Havasu, 73
Lake Perris, SWP East Branch terminal reservoir, 119, 122
Lamm, Benny, 61, 62
Las Virgenes Municipal Water District, 87
Lauten, John, 199
Lawrence Adit, 71
Lee Ferry, Arizona, 40
Leeds, Albert, 174
Levees, delta, 138-140, 142, 144
Locke, California, 140
Long Beach, City of, 43
Los Angeles, 9, 15-24, 43, 98, 104; Aqueduct, building of, 19-23; Los Angeles Water Company, 15, 16, 17, 18; Department of Water and Power, city water supply, 67, 105, 159, 160, 161; population growth, 11-12, 17, 24
Los Angeles Times, 3, 156
Los Banos Grandes Reservoir, 158
Lyman, Richard, 50

M

Marin County, 151, 156
Marshall, Colonel Robert, 98, 100, 103
Marshall, James, 11, 93
Marshall Plan, 98, 100
Martin, Les, 54, 62
Mathews, W.B., 58, 88-89
Merced River, 138
Merriman, Thaddeus, 50
Merrithew, Bill, 61, 66
Metropolitan Water District: board of directors, current, v; board of directors, founding (photo only), 42; chairmen of the board, 189-194; general managers, 195-201; founding charge, 183; original member cities, 43; incorporation, 42-43
Mexico, rights to use of Colorado River water, 81-83
Million Dollar Theater, MWD headquarters, 88
Mills, Henry J. "Hank", 59, 62, 108, 198
Missions, Southern California history, 9-11
Moeur, Arizona Governor B.B., 72-73
Mokelumne Aqueduct and River, 98, 138, 142
Mono Lake and Basin, 159, 161
Mother Lode, 93, 123, 138
Muir, John, 97
Mulholland, William, 15-24, 25, 42, 45-46; 67
Municipal Water District of Orange County, 87

N

Nadeau, Remi, 15
New Hope Cross Channel, 157
New River, 36
Nixon, Richard, 147
North and South Bay Aqueducts (SWP), 120

O

Oakland, water development, 98
Oroville Dam, 104, 105, 118, 120, 122, 123-125
Owen, Langdon, 131, 133
Owens Valley and Mono Basin, 18-20, 23, 98, 159, 161
Ozone process, 178, 179

P

Palm Springs, California, 169
Palo Verde Irrigation District, 167
Parker Dam, 67, 72, 73, 82-83

Parker route, 45-46, 57
Pasadena, City of, 43
Pasadena Star News, 2
Patton, General George S., 78-81
Peripheral Canal, 122, 133-135, 149-157, 185, 204, 205
PEROXONE, 178, 179
Phillips, Robert, 67, 69
Pinchot, Chief of Forest Service Gifford, 19
Population growth in California, 4, 7, 11-12, 17, 24, 78, 84, 87, 103-104, 119, 148, 172, 183, 184
Porter, Assemblyman Carley, 111, 112, 118
Potrero Creek, 185
Potrero shaft, San Jacinto Tunnel, 69-70, 71
Powell, John Wesley, 25, 33-35
Preston, Al, 46-48, 61, 72
Proposition W, 88, 129
Proposition 1 (1960), 112-113, 118, 205
Proposition 8 (1980), 154-155, 156
Proposition 9 (1982), 155, 156, 157
Pumping plants, 57, 62, 68, 75, 76

Q

Quality, water, testing for, 173-179

R

Rainfall distrubution, 92
Reagan, Ronald, governor, 133-134, 150; president, 147
Reber Plan, 144, 145
Rifkind, Special Master Simon, U.S. Supreme Court, 163
Rio Grande River, 82-83
Robie, Ronald, 149, 150, 152
Rockwood, Charles, 36
Rommel, Field Marshal Erwin, 79
Roosevelt, Franklin D., 78, 85, 101
Roosevelt, President Theodore, 19
Rose, Mark, 38
Rose Parade, MWD float, 2
Rosseti, Victor, 86, 189

S

Sacramento River, 37, 95-96, 98, 100, 138, 153
Safe Drinking Water Act (1974), 174, 176
Salt water intrusion, 140
Salton Sea, 36, 38, 163, 165
Salyer Land Company, 155
San Andreas fault, 51, 126
San Bernardino, City of, 43
San Diego, 92, 118, 164, 202
San Diego County Water Authority, 84-86, 203, 206
San Fernando, City of, 87
San Fernando Tunnel, 129
San Francisco, 96, 107, 115, 156,
San Francisco Bay, 131, 137, 138, 144, 145, 153, 158
San Francisco Chronicle, 117, 156
San Jacinto Tunnel, 67, 69, 71, 76
San Joaquin River, 95-96
San Joaquin Valley, 100, 104, 106, 115, 120, 122, 125, 126, 155-156, 158, 169
San Juan Project, 51
San Luis Reservoir, 107, 120
San Marino, City of, 43
Santa Ana, City of, 43
Santa Barbara, California, 159
Santa Clara Valley Water District, 134
Sawyer, Judge Lorenzo, 95
Schultz, Walter, 130
Scotland, East Kilbride, 128
Senate Bill 200, 152, 153, 154, 155 (see Prop. 9)
Senate Bill 346, 151, 152
Sepulveda Feeder, 129
Seven Cities of Cibola, 28-30
Shasta Dam, 100, 140, 153
Shreves, Chuck, 164
Sierra Club, 97
Siphons, 22-23, 66, 68, 74
Skinner, Robert, 57, 59, 85, 113, 115, 116, 197
Smith, Congressman Sylvester, 19
Smith River, 153
South Bay Aqueduct, 134
Southern sea level route, 51
Spring Valley Water Company, 97
St. Francis Dam, 15
Stanislaus River, 138
State Water Fund, 111
State Water Plan of 1931, 100, 106
State Water Project, 89, 91, 103, 110; contract negotiations, 113-117; 118; construction, 119-128; 142, 150, 151, 156, 157, 159, 160, 161, 168-169, 174, 180, 181, 182, 184, 185, 187, 202, 203, 204, 205
State Water Resources Control Board, 149, 163, 166
Stockton, California, 140
Stringfellow, Ralph "Pistol Pete", 63, 64
Subsisdence, 104, 140,
Suisun Marsh, 153
Swing-Johnson legislative team, 41
Swing, Congressman Phil, 38, 39, 40, 41
Sylmar earthquake, 87, 129

T

Teerink, John, 106, 107, 135
Tehachapi Mountains, 106, 121, 126-128, 134, 180
Texas, 82-83
Thirst (film), 54
Thomason, Sam, 66, 74,
Three Valleys Municipal Water District, 87
Torrance, City of, 43
Tracy, California, 120, 133
Tracy Pumping Plant (CVP), 142
Tree-ring research, 37
Trihalomethanes (THMs), 174, 175
Trinity River, 153,
Tunnels, 23, 57, 59, 63, 66, 67, 68, 69, 70, 71, 76
Tuolumne River, 97, 138, 142
Tuthill, Lewis (Tuthill Tech), 74

U

Upper San Gabriel Valley Municipal Water District, 87, 170
U.S. Army Corps of Engineers, 35, 95, 104
U.S. Army Topographical Engineers, 32
U.S. Geological Survey, 98
U.S. Navy, 85
U.S. Reclamation Service, 19

V

Vail Lake, 185

W

Ward, Carl E., 203, 204, 205, 207
Warne, William, 122, 123, 125, 126, 128
Water quality laboratory, 177
Water quality tasting panel, 176-177
Water quality testing, 173, 176, 177
Waterway Control Plan, 131
West Basin Municipal Water District, 86, 203, 205, 207
West Branch (SWP), 121, 134, 199
West Portal, San Jacinto Tunnel, 71, 76
Western Municipal Water District of Riverside County, 87
Westlands Water District, 110
Weymouth filtration plant, 81, 173, 177
Weymouth, Frank E., 49-50, 52, 57-59, 66, 67, 71, 77, 88, 173, 195-196
Whitewater River, 169
Whitlock, Don, 116
Whitsett, W.P., 43, 189
Wide Canyon Number 2, 68
Wild and scenic river system, 153-154
Wiley, A.J., 50
Will, Robert P., 171
Wilson, Governor Pete, 158
Witt, Ray, 45, 48
Wood, Clyde, 74-75
Woodruff vs. North Bloomfield. 95
Wozencraft, Dr. Oliver, 35
Wyoming vs. Colorado, 38

Y

Yosemite National Park, 97
Young, Brigham, 34

Z

Zanjas, 16
Zanjeros, 16
Zapp, Jack, 59, 69, 71